The
DIGITAL ERA

1995 TO 2010

Reader's
Digest

Published by The Reader's Digest Association, Inc.
London • New York • Sydney • Montreal

Contents

Introduction

As the third millennium dawned, the developed nations of the world appeared to be swept up in an unprecedented euphoria. The much-hyped 'millennium bug' had not, as some had predicted, produced computer meltdown and people seemed hooked on an addictive new digital drug – the Internet. The information society stimulated economic growth, and in this new virtual reality the World Wide Web forged connections between people on a scale that no language, religion or political ideology had ever achieved.

A brief period of stability proved to be the calm before the storm. On 11 September, 2001, any confidence in the future in the West was rudely shattered by the terrifying sight of hijacked commercial aeroplanes plunging into the Twin Towers of the World Trade Center in New York and the Pentagon in Washington DC, taking thousands of innocent lives. The spectre of global terrorism was countered by the US-led 'war on terror', which rode roughshod over long-cherished ideals of liberty, solidarity and fraternity. New powers arose, new alliances were formed

China looks to the future
The concourse of Shanghai's World Exposition of 2010. At the exhibition's heart was this giant spaceship-like construction, a fitting centrepiece for a host nation embarking on space exploration. In a world facing many problems, not least a rapidly growing human population, the theme of the exhibition was how to improve urban life.

on the world stage, and international security and diplomacy struggled to deal with so-called 'rogue states' from Iran to North Korea, declared by US President George W Bush to be an 'axis of evil'.

Meanwhile, the European Union continued to grow, reaching 27 member states, as the balance of the world shifted. China became the world's second-largest economy; Russia, Brazil and India also emerged as major economic players; and the G8 economic group of nations expanded into the G20. As ever, green shoots of optimism began to reappear.

The divisive sectarianism and racism that blighted many Western societies was rebuffed by America's election of its first mixed-race president, Barack Obama, in 2008. Even after the financial crisis that blew up that same year, with devastating ongoing conseqences, individuals and states continue to respond to humanitarian disasters with generous aid donations. Research into ways of combatting global warming and climate change testifies to human ingenuity and adaptability. As scientists endeavour to find 'green' solutions for a world that will one day run out of oil, the hope is that technology will prove to be the saviour of our planet.

The editors

◀ Dolly the Sheep, born in 1996, was the first mammal to be cloned from an adult cell, raising the prospect of therapeutic cloning

▼ The Internet and associated developments such as WiFi have opened new possibilities for teleworking, prompting the European Union to issue a report in 2002 recommending more widespread acceptance of flexible working practices

WORK IN A WIRELESS

▲ Although geolocation systems were pioneered by the Americans with their introduction of GPS – the receiver above is from 1997 – Europe is catching up with its own Galileo system, due to be fully on stream by 2014

The 21st century began with a paradox: never before had people enjoyed so much prosperity and so many material goods, yet at the same time the world's economy was becoming ever more ephemeral and virtual. Widespread digitisation has seen

today's TV screens range from huge high-definition LCD and plasma devices to displays on mobile phones

▼ Shopping changed for ever in the 1990s with the advent of online ordering of goods delivered by courier direct to the customer's door

telemarket.fr
Tellement plus que vos courses

market
permarché online
0 825 813 813

AIRPORT

► The Tamagotchi virtual pet, launched in 1996, was snapped up by a generation enthralled by technological innovation

all kinds of content – music, films, books, even whole libraries – gradually liberated from physical media and put online. This has created an immense digital database where masses of material is permanently available and accessible, thanks to efficient search

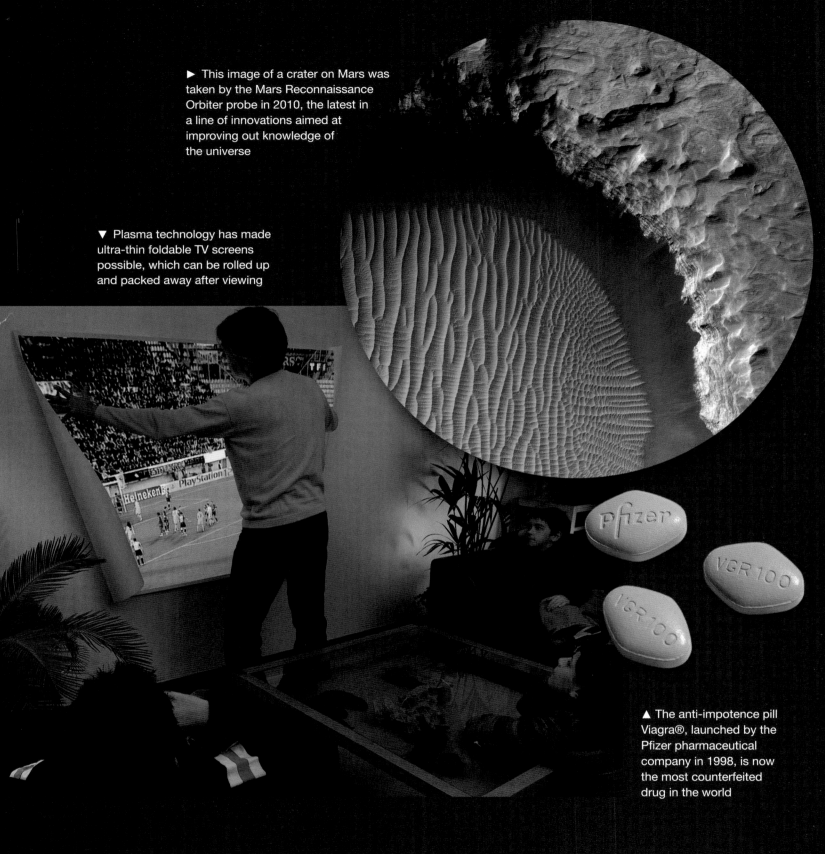

► This image of a crater on Mars was taken by the Mars Reconnaissance Orbiter probe in 2010, the latest in a line of innovations aimed at improving out knowledge of the universe

▼ Plasma technology has made ultra-thin foldable TV screens possible, which can be rolled up and packed away after viewing

▲ The anti-impotence pill Viagra®, launched by the Pfizer pharmaceutical company in 1998, is now the most counterfeited drug in the world

engines, while high-speed broadband and WiFi make it instantly downloadable to a computer or mobile phone. Encyclopedias can be consulted at the click of a mouse, while wireless networks and smartphones allow people to access the Internet from

Wi-Fi

∗ hot spot

new ways of making you talk™

▲ WiFi networks have made it possible to access the Internet in the most unlikely of places, freeing users from the need to be physically connected to cable or phone line

▶ Digital file compression formats, such as MP3, opened up new possibilities for downloading music and listening on the move

▲ The Toyota Prius, launched in 1997 as the world's first production-line hybrid car, switches automatically between an electric motor and a conventional engine

wherever they happen to be. With iPods for music and readers for e-books and digital newspapers, entertainment and information is becoming ever-more mobile. As a result, new ways of working are emerging in the form of telecommuting, as well as new modes of

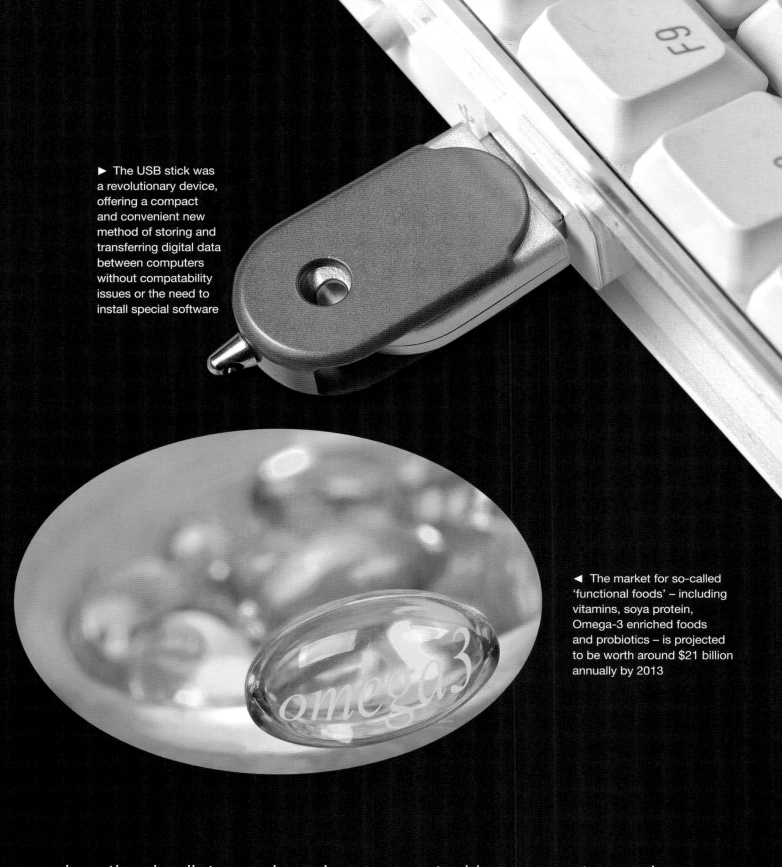

▶ The USB stick was a revolutionary device, offering a compact and convenient new method of storing and transferring digital data between computers without compatability issues or the need to install special software

◀ The market for so-called 'functional foods' – including vitamins, soya protein, Omega-3 enriched foods and probiotics – is projected to be worth around $21 billion annually by 2013

education in distance learning supported by computer and new ways of shopping in e-commerce. The real power of the brave new digital network is in its collaborative nature: today, anyone can be a musician, a writer or a film-maker, and post their work on

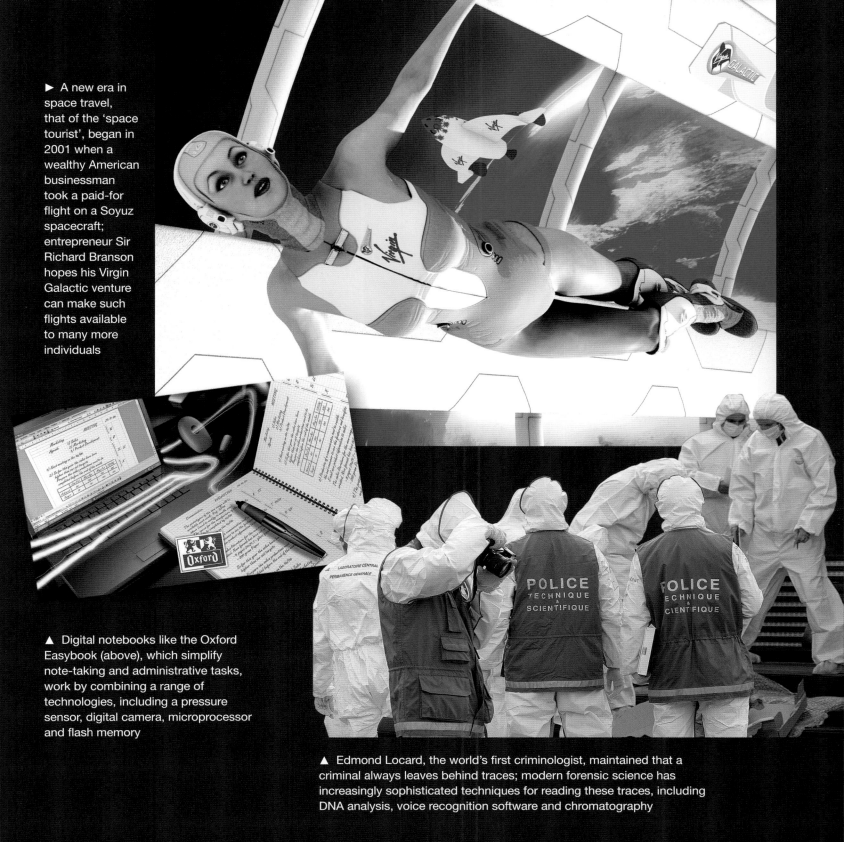

▶ A new era in space travel, that of the 'space tourist', began in 2001 when a wealthy American businessman took a paid-for flight on a Soyuz spacecraft; entrepreneur Sir Richard Branson hopes his Virgin Galactic venture can make such flights available to many more individuals

▲ Digital notebooks like the Oxford Easybook (above), which simplify note-taking and administrative tasks, work by combining a range of technologies, including a pressure sensor, digital camera, microprocessor and flash memory

▲ Edmond Locard, the world's first criminologist, maintained that a criminal always leaves behind traces; modern forensic science has increasingly sophisticated techniques for reading these traces, including DNA analysis, voice recognition software and chromatography

file-sharing platforms, or exchange ideas via social networking sites. Although the younger generation seems to have abandoned television in favour of the Web, the small screen has found a new technological lease of life through high definition and 3D.

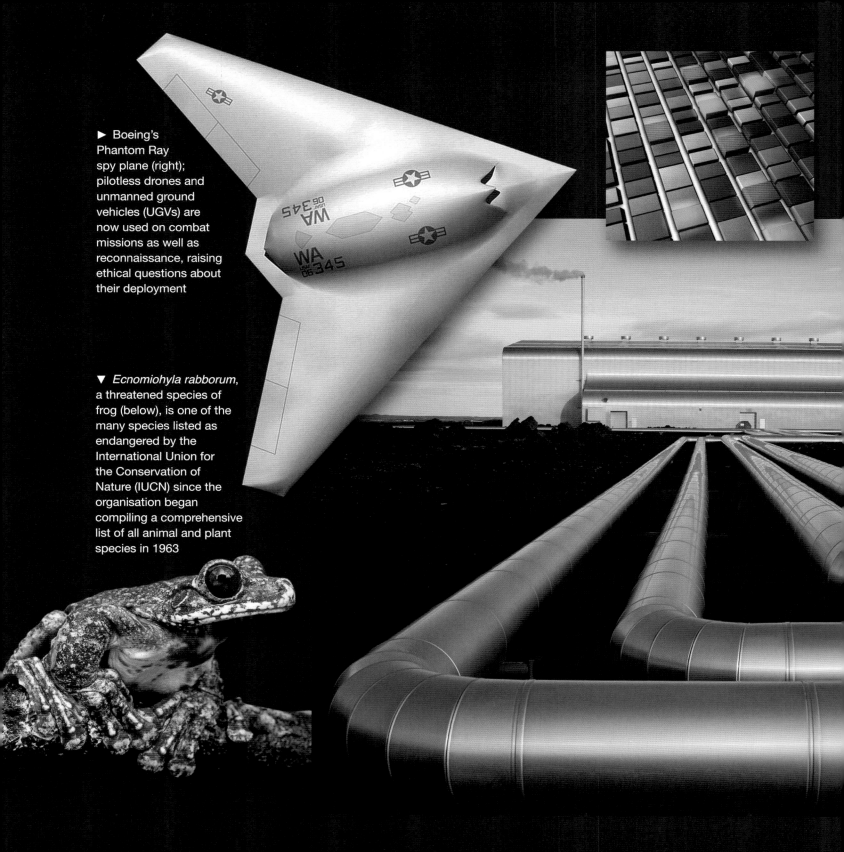

▶ Boeing's Phantom Ray spy plane (right); pilotless drones and unmanned ground vehicles (UGVs) are now used on combat missions as well as reconnaissance, raising ethical questions about their deployment

▼ *Ecnomiohyla rabborum*, a threatened species of frog (below), is one of the many species listed as endangered by the International Union for the Conservation of Nature (IUCN) since the organisation began compiling a comprehensive list of all animal and plant species in 1963

Meanwhile, forensic science has devised ingenious ways of solving seemingly uncrackable crimes – largely thanks to the advent of DNA testing. Another modern marvel is GPS, which enables people to pinpoint their position anywhere on the planet – though

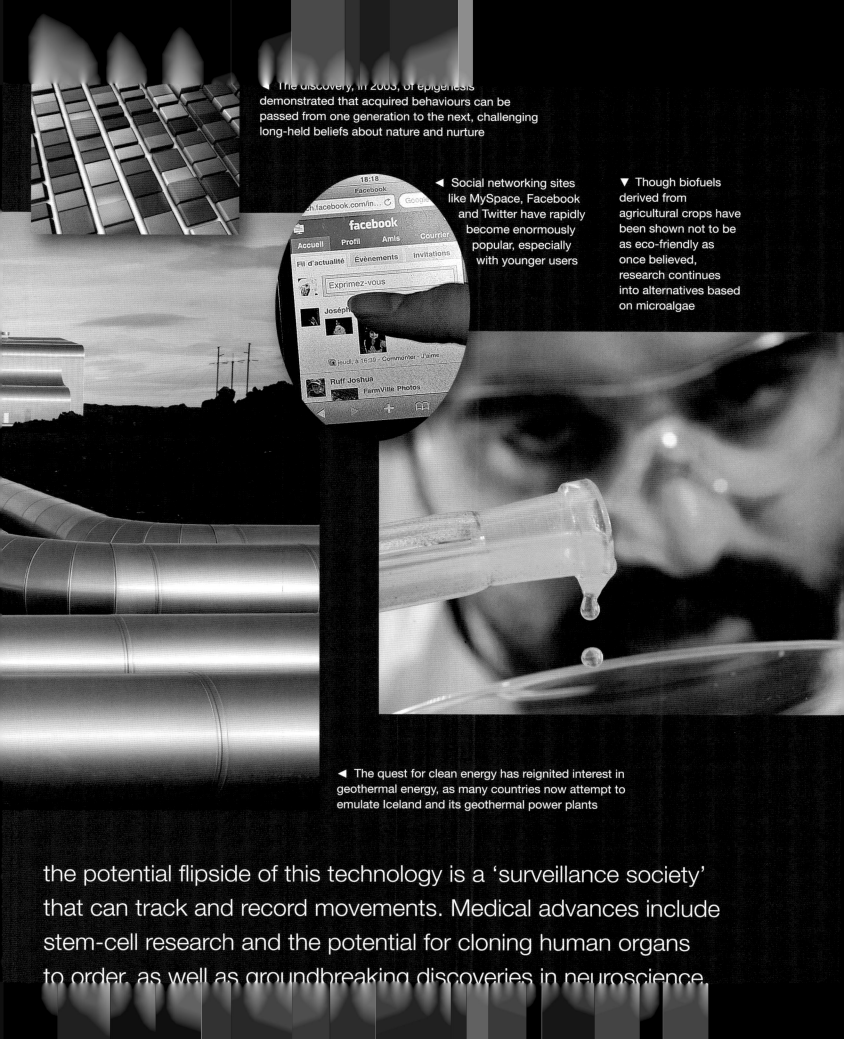

The discovery, in 2003, of epigenesis demonstrated that acquired behaviours can be passed from one generation to the next, challenging long-held beliefs about nature and nurture

◄ Social networking sites like MySpace, Facebook and Twitter have rapidly become enormously popular, especially with younger users

▼ Though biofuels derived from agricultural crops have been shown not to be as eco-friendly as once believed, research continues into alternatives based on microalgae

◄ The quest for clean energy has reignited interest in geothermal energy, as many countries now attempt to emulate Iceland and its geothermal power plants

the potential flipside of this technology is a 'surveillance society' that can track and record movements. Medical advances include stem-cell research and the potential for cloning human organs to order, as well as groundbreaking discoveries in neuroscience,

▲ As astronomers use giant telescopes, like Keck II on Hawaii (above), to look deep into space, they are also gazing back through time towards the origins of the Universe and the Big Bang

▲ The severe drought that hit southwestern China in March 2010 (above) was just one of a series of natural disasters in the early 21st century thought to have been brought on by climate change

▶ The first prosthetic arm to be controlled by a person's brain was unveiled in 2006, the fruit of advances in neuroscience and surgery

But undoubtedly the greatest challenge of the age is global warming; the threat that this poses to our planet has stimulated research not just into 'clean' (if controversial) energy solutions such as geothermal and biofuels, but also into energy-efficient vehicles

◄ There is no predicting what will a hit on YouTube, th video-sharing websi launched in 2005; Matthew Harding (le became an Internet celebrity through clips of him dancing in front of well-know landmarks around the world

True Compass: A Memoir

mutually competitive, with an intensity that owed more to joy than to an urge for dominance. These values flowed into us on the energies of Joseph and Rose Kennedy. They helped us form bonds among one another, and to develop personalities based on those bonds, to an extent that remains to this day under-appreciated by the chronicler of my family. They sustain me still. They lie at the heart of the story I wish to tell.

I was nine years old in that summer I wish to tell. summer of the familiar world into which I was born. I was not clear why we had all come back home from England, but I was happy that we had. I was too young to fully understand that my father had resigned his ambassadorship. I was certainly too young to comprehend that he'd resigned because he had offended some people in England by saying that the British might not be capable of fighting a war against Germany. It would have been news to me that Dad had displeased President Roosevelt with these same remarks. Or that when he was away from the Cape house that summer, in New York and Washington, he was trying to persuade other people to join his effort at keeping America out of the war. Or that, despite their differences, Joseph Kennedy continued to support Franklin Roosevelt as president.

I just knew that on weekends, he and I would ride horseback together on the Cape, and that was all I really cared to know.

It's hardly surprising that these facets of my father's life were unknowable to me as a child. If my father were alive

▲ Former fighter pilot Yves Rossy made a splash as 'Jetman' in 2006 when he made his maiden flight with his jet-powered flying wing

▲ Digital e-book readers first appeared in 1998, but are only now having a real impact on the book market; the page above is on an Apple iPad of 2010

powered by hybrid engines, electric motors or fuel cells. In the more distant future, nuclear fusion holds out the tantalising prospect of an unlimited, clean and safe source of energy. Looking far beyond the concerns of our own planet, giant telescopes have

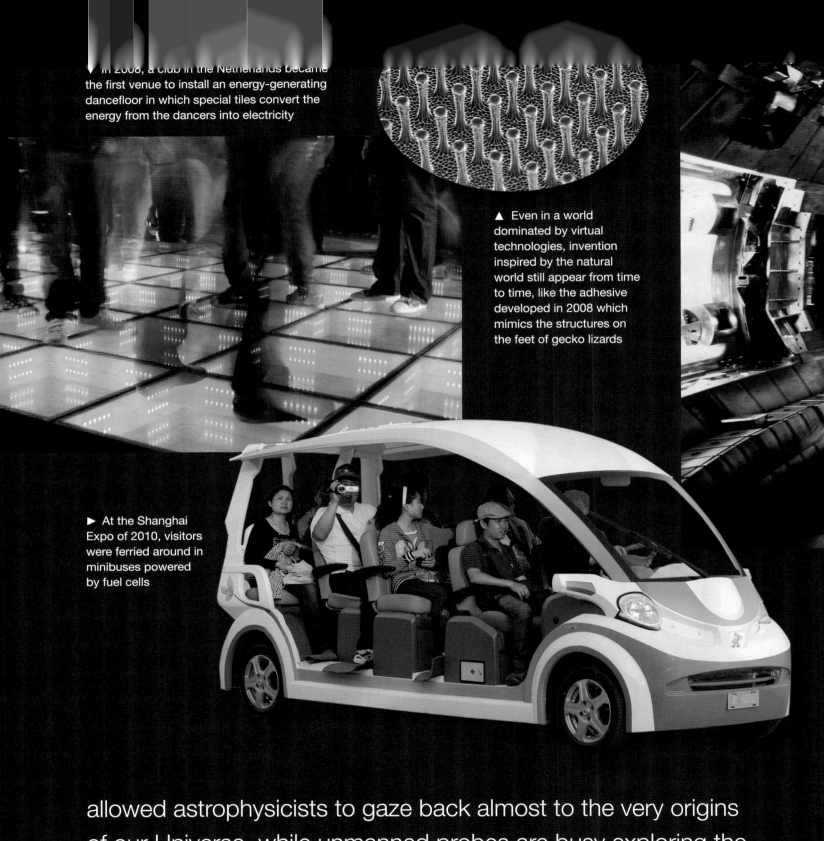

In 2008, a club in the Netherlands became the first venue to install an energy-generating dancefloor in which special tiles convert the energy from the dancers into electricity

▲ Even in a world dominated by virtual technologies, invention inspired by the natural world still appear from time to time, like the adhesive developed in 2008 which mimics the structures on the feet of gecko lizards

► At the Shanghai Expo of 2010, visitors were ferried around in minibuses powered by fuel cells

allowed astrophysicists to gaze back almost to the very origins of our Universe, while unmanned probes are busy exploring the farthest reaches of the Solar System and beyond. The rise of space tourism promises to write a new chapter in extraterrestrial

▲ In 2010 construction commenced on a revolutionary new reactor in the south of France, a joint international venture aimed at bringing power from nuclear fusion a step nearer

◄ The Chinese pavilion at the 2010 World Exposition hosted by Shanghai, the commercial capital of the People's Republic of China, with the theme of sustainable urban development

travel. Many of the innovative technologies that will shape the 21st century and beyond were showcased in the first great international Expo of the new millennium – significantly held in Shanghai in China, the rising star in the world economy

THE STORY OF INVENTIONS

At a stroke, the creation of GPS made compasses and sextants obsolete: with its network of tracking satellites, GPS could instantly tell people where they were to within just a few metres, and help them find their way to their destination. But if this technology enabled humanity to get its bearings physically, making getting lost a thing of the past, the story was rather different where the destiny of the planet was concerned. Climate change, food security and the ethical dimensions of cloning are just three of the major challenges facing the technologists of the future.

GPS – 1995

Pinpointing our position

In April 1995, some months after the final satellite in the NAVSTAR constellation had been put into orbit around the Earth, the navigational aid known as the Global Positioning System – GPS for short – became operational. Anyone with a GPS receiver could now instantly discover their precise location on the Earth's surface. Mobile phones are now equipped with this function, but the complex GPS system remains costly to maintain.

Magellan the navigator
The GPS 3000 receiver (right), made by the Magellan Corporation of California in 1997, found a ready market among mountaineers and yachtsmen.

Radio navigation made huge strides during the Second World War, but coverage was limited by the number of terrestrial transmitting stations that could be set up. Also, despite the fact that the aerials were perched on top of towers hundreds of metres tall, the curvature of the Earth restricted the range of the radio transmitters. In 1957 the launch of Sputnik 1, the world's first man-made satellite, opened up the potential for placing radio navigation stations in orbit, thus overcoming the problems of range and installation. This heralded the birth of GPS. The system would eventually came into being through a long sequence of piecemeal technological advances.

Three-dimensional plotting

In 1960 the US Air Force introduced MOSAIC (MObile System for Accurate ICBM Control), a traditional radio-navigation system, but crucially one that enabled users to plot their position in three dimensions: latitude, longitude and altitude. This was a vital function for aircraft. Further studies led, in 1963, to a proposal for orbiting transmitting stations. Creating such a system would be a huge undertaking, but this was the height of the Cold War, when the perceived threat of a nuclear strike against the USA outweighed all objections. The ability to launch a retaliatory strike required an accurate guidance system for American bombers, missiles and nuclear-armed submarines. On

Early GPS
A ground-based receiver (left), built by the German Prakla-Seismos company, which was among the first pieces of equipment used to test the GPS satellites launched in 1978.

3 May, 1967, Timation-1 was launched by the US navy; equipped with an atomic clock, this was the first satellite to broadcast an accurate time reference for use as a ranging signal to ground receivers. In 1973 the Pentagon opted for a Defense Navigation Satellite System (DNSS), the real genesis of what would later become GPS. The first set of ten satellites were put into orbit to test the system between 1978 and 1985. Four years later, launch of the NAVSTAR constellation of orbiting satellites began, making the system fully operational.

ACCURACY IN SPACE

GPS originally relied on a model of the Earth's surface that has become a yardstick for cartography: WGS 84 (World Geodetic System 1984). But although this was extremely accurate for latitudinal and longitudinal measurements, it was less so where altitude was concerned. As a result, modern GPS receivers use another model, the Earth Gravity Model 1996, which has overcome the altitude errors. In practice, however, such inaccuracies did not pose any danger, since all aircraft have their own altimeters anyway, while other vehicles and personal users rarely need to know their precise altitude.

ACCURACY IN TIME

Travelling at the speed of light (300,000km/s), radio signals take just tens of milliseconds to reach the Earth from a satellite. As a result, it would be impossible to work out the precise duration of a transmission from a satellite to a receiver without an extraordinarily exact time reference. It is no coincidence that the GPS project was only able to get underway after atomic clocks had been sent into space on 'Timation' satellites. GPS time, as set by the master control station at Colorado Springs, commenced on 6 January, 1980, at 0 hrs 00 minutes precisely. Even though this was not its original function, the precision and universal accessibility of GPS have made it a benchmark for all kinds of activities that rely on split-second timing.

The original intention for GPS was that it would have a purely military application, but this changed following an avoidable tragedy. On 1 September, 1983, a Korean Airlines Boeing 747 unintentionally strayed into Soviet restricted airspace and was shot down by a Sukhoi Su-15 fighter, killing all 269 passengers and crew on board. This prompted US President Ronald Reagan to declare that GPS should be freely available for civilian use.

How GPS works

There are three stages, or segments, in a GPS system: satellites, control stations and receivers. Today, a total of 24 satellites across six orbital planes at altitudes of up to 20,000 kilometres cover the entire surface of the Earth. These transmit extremely precise radio time signals. Six earth stations sited around the globe, including a master control station at Colorado Springs, permanently monitor the operation and exact position of the satellites and readjust their onboard clocks to GPS time; any deviation, however slight, is unacceptable. The Earth stations transmit this information to the satellites, which rebroadcast it to the receivers. Thanks to the absolute precision of the system, whenever a receiver on Earth picks up a signal from a satellite, it can measure the time taken by the radio waves to reach it, and use this to determine the distance they have travelled. Since each receiver is

Ringing the Earth
An artist's impression of the 24 NAVSTAR (NAVigation System with Timing And Ranging) satellites and the path of their orbits (above).

Pre-launch tests
Technicians testing the deployment of a NAVSTAR satellite's solar panels (right). Each satellite has a span of 5.2m, weighs 900kg and has a transmission power of 50W. The operational life of a satellite is ten years.

in simultaneous contact with at least four satellites, it can then work out its position in relation to them. Since it also picks up information on where precisely those satellites are positioned around the Earth and has an image of the Earth's surface stored in its memory, it can then pinpoint its own location.

Open access

From 1993 onwards, this system, which was developed for use by the US military, has been freely available for civilian use throughout the entire world. Inevitably, the armed forces of

Secure underground location
The Colorado Springs GPS facility (above), constructed at the height of the Cold War, is buried inside a mountain range, up to 600m below the surface, and protected by armoured doors that weigh 20 tonnes and can withstand a nuclear blast. After the Cold War ended, the facility was considered too expensive to run and was mothballed in 2006; however, it can be reactivated within an hour if need be.

AN IMPORTANT PRECURSOR

In 1971, the US Navy and US Air Force unveiled a radio-navigation system known as OMEGA. Like traditional systems, it used terrestrial transmission stations, but it had one important difference: the carrier wave of the signal was set at a very low frequency (VLF). This type of wave is both restricted and directed by the Earth's atmosphere, so it was straightforward to transmit it around the entire world and obtain global coverage using just eight land-based stations. OMEGA was the first truly worldwide radio-navigation network, and was used extensively both by civil agencies and the United States Coast Guard. It was rendered obsolete by GPS and shut down on 30 September, 1997.

foreign countries, some of them not necessarily friendly, also make use of the system. To maintain their advantage, the Americans came up with a clever ruse: the satellites transmit two types of carrier signal: the P ('precision') code modulation, extremely accurate but encrypted, was reserved for the US military and certain government agencies, while the C/A ('coarse acquisition') code, deliberately degraded but accurate to within 100 metres, was accessible by the general public.

On 1 May, 2000, US President Bill Clinton announced that this 'selective availability' would be turned off, giving everyone access to accurate GPS. In fact, an enhanced form called 'Differential GPS' was by then already giving general users military precision. Nowadays, a civilian receiver can easily pinpoint an individual's position to within 5 metres.

Galileo, Glonass and other systems

Yet GPS remained dependent on the goodwill of the US military, which could at any time decide to scramble the signal. For this reason, the European Union decided to fund and put in place a similar global system. Under the aegis of the EU and the European Space Agency, Galileo will provide a range of services, some highly precise and offered through subscription for use by air transport and the emergency services, plus a free service for the public giving an accuracy of better than 5 metres. Two satellites in the Galileo system – the first of a planned constellation of 30 – went into space on a Russian Soyuz rocket launched from French Guiana in October 2011. The free civil navigation service is due to start in 2014, with specialised services being rolled out over the rest of the decade. A US-European cooperation agreement, signed in June 2004, means that GPS and Galileo could be accessed interchangeably by the same receiver.

The Russian Glonass system of 24 satellites has been up and running since 1996. Glonass deteriorated after the break-up of the Soviet Union and by 2010, with just 21 satellites working (and two in reserve), it was struggling to provide global coverage. There are plans to overhaul and upgrade it. The Chinese BeiDou navigation system, which was introduced in

Hi-tech soldiers
Modern infantry use a host of electronic aids, such as helmets equipped with real-time positioning and goggles with light amplifiers for improved night vision. Here (left), two French soldiers are using the FELIN system introduced into the French armed forces in 2008.

1993, will ultimately comprise 30 satellites providing global coverage from 2017. The second generation of the system, still under construction, will be known as Compass. India's IRNSS facility, a local system using seven satellites, will be operational from 2014.

Finally, with its Quasi-Zenith Satellite System (2013), Japan has taken an original approach. Rather than trying to replace GPS, the three satellites in this array, fixed in a limited orbit above the region, are designed to augment the quality of the GPS signal: the longer the access a receiver has to a satellite, the better its positioning accuracy will be.

European facility
One of the navigation satellites for the European Galileo network as revealed in a computer-generated image. The system's 30 satellites will be launched by the European Space Agency's Ariane rocket and will orbit at over 23,000km above the Earth.

DIFFERENTIAL GPS

Prior to 2000, the GPS signal (C/A) that was available for non-military applications was not sufficiently accurate for use in air navigation, search-and-rescue operations, or surveying. As a result, US bodies such as the Federal Aviation Authority (FAA) and the US Coast Guard enhanced it by applying Differential GPS (DGPS) technology. This is based on a network of fixed, ground-based local reference stations that receive the GPS signal. These work out and broadcast the difference between the position indicated by the satellite and their known fixed position, thus correcting errors in the C/A signal. Any handheld GPS receiver within 200 nautical miles of a DGPS station will have access to the same satellites and, so long as it has the capacity to pick up the station's broadcast, will also be able to compensate for these inaccuracies. DPGS signals are accurate to about 3 metres – more precise than the military's P-code signal.

MILITARY USES OF GPS

The advent of the Global Positioning System network has transformed the modern battlefield. GPS is embedded into integrated infantry combat systems used by ground troops, enabling soldiers to locate their objective even in unknown terrain, in adverse weather conditions or in total darkness. Installed in weapons systems on board military vehicles or aircraft, GPS can be used to track potential targets, flag them as hostile and transmit their coordinates to precision-guided ('smart') bombs, missiles or other munitions. It is this capability that has led military planners and journalists to speak of 'surgical strikes'. The system has also become a vital tool in search-and-rescue missions for pilots shot down over enemy territory: a GPS receiver now forms part of the standard survival kit for aircrew, allowing them to send their precise position to helicopter-borne recovery teams.

In-Car Navaid
SatNav devices in cars (above) use GPS data to tell drivers the fastest route in real time and the one that will be most fuel-efficient. They can also show the location of fixed speed-cameras.

GPS in civilian use

GPS was designed as a military application, but before long the C/A code signal, augmented by Differential GPS, was being harnessed in several specialised civilian realms of activity. These included transport systems, emergency and rescue services, transportation of dangerous materials, plus technical and scientific disciplines that required precise timing and location-finding, such as surveying and earthquake monitoring.

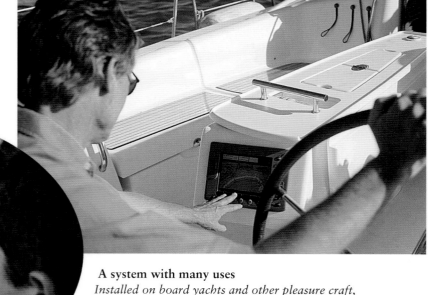

A system with many uses
Installed on board yachts and other pleasure craft, GPS receivers have become a vital navigational tool for boat skippers (above). They are also found on board combine-harvesters (left): a GPS system can plot a map of the relative yield from different fields, or even parts of fields, and from this generate a chart showing where more, or less, fertiliser is needed for the next crop.

As miniaturisation made GPS receivers less unwieldy – and as the price came down – they caught on fast with the general public. The first groups to adopt them were amateur yachtsmen and hikers. Later, GPS receivers became widespread in cars in the form of SatNav devices and began to be integrated into mobile phones. Since general users are not normally interested in plotting their exact geographical position in pure terms of latitude, longitude and altitude, the types of receivers that they use are linked to maps for route-finding, to information on traffic flow, or in the case of mobile phones to directory services. People can use their mobiles to find out information on, say, the nearest restaurant and then call it to make a reservation. In modern usage, 'GPS' has come to denote all sorts of different spin-off functions that operate through the GPS system. Tens of millions of such devices are now in circulation.

A 'BIG BROTHER' DEVICE?

Some people are concerned that the proliferation of personal GPS receivers in car SatNavs and mobile phones risks creating a 'Big Brother' society, where everyone is under surveillance. This simply is not the case, since GPS receivers are passive systems: in other words, they do not emit a signal and so cannot be traced. Yet systems do exist that transmit their location to a central facility, for instance via a mobile phone network. Such a function is useful for control centres monitoring fleets of emergency vehicles, say, or taxis, or even integrated logistics systems tracking the movements of lorries. Some mobile phone companies offer this service as a special option to individual users – for example, to parents of children with cellphones who want to keep tabs on their whereabouts.

GPS forms a key part of Emergency Locator Transmitters (ELTs), beacons that are activated by yachts or aircraft (or individuals) in distress, which emit traceable signals to guide the emergency services. By giving the exact location, GPS saves vital time spent searching and so can save lives. But even here, although the position is indicated by the GPS, it is not this system but rather an active radio signal that transmits the information to the search-and-rescue team.

Traveller's friend
A tourist using the GPS function on his mobile phone to find his way around an unfamiliar city (right). Miniaturisation has led to GPS watches designed for joggers, who can now hook up to a satellite in less than a minute: they show the distance run, average speed and the course of the route. There are even gloves for skiers with an embedded GPS function.

Global Positioning System

Without certain key technological advances – radio in the 19th century; satellites, IT and the atomic clock in the 20th – GPS would never have seen the light of day. The system now covers the entire surface of the globe.

RADIO NAVIGATION
FROM RADIO BEACONS TO SATELLITES

The idea of using radio transmissions to help ships to navigate was first mooted at the beginning of the 20th century. The earliest systems used radio beacons – powerful fixed transmitters sited at strategic locations. The aerials were, and still are, located on top of towers hundreds of metres tall in order to maximise their range. Ships equipped with directional receivers and radio direction-finding apparatus (radiogoniometers) could triangulate their position simply by locating several radio beacons simultaneously. During the Second World War, hyperbolic systems began to appear, such as LORAN (LOng RAnge Navigation) and the Decca Navigator System, which worked by measuring the time difference between receipt of signals from a pair of radio transmitters. GPS took its cue from these later systems, but with transmission stations in orbit. In certain maritime zones, LORAN has been kept as back-up in case the GPS signal fails.

The automated defence system on this US Navy vessel uses GPS to spot and track incoming missiles

A portable GPS receiver made by Magellan in 2000

GEOLOCATION
FROM SPUTNIK TO NAVSTAR

In 1957 the USSR launched Sputnik 1, the first artificial satellite to orbit the Earth. By tracking the bleeping radio signal transmitted by Sputnik, scientists in the USA found that its frequency was changing, just like the sound of an ambulance siren approaching then receding (the Doppler Effect); this enabled them to work out roughly where the satellite was at any given time. The first formal geolocation experiment was conducted in the early 1960s using five satellites and the Doppler principle. Sputnik 1 and its successors thus contributed to the birth of GPS in two key ways: as orbiting platforms that could receive transmitting stations, and because they could be pinpointed by studying their own radio signals.

MAPPING THE EARTH'S SURFACE
FROM THE MAPPA MUNDI TO THE GEOID

Measuring the precise dimensions and the exact form of the Earth's surface is the business of a branch of science known as geodesy, which has been in existence since mapping began. The outlines of continents and the courses of rivers were determined by traditional cartographic means – by dead reckoning, star sightings and, for short distances, by triangulation. The advent of the first theodolites and goniometers hugely improved the range and accuracy of the old method of triangulation. This was the technique used between 1792 and 1798 to measure the quarter-meridian between Dunkirk and Barcelona, which determined the length of the standard metre. Nowadays, thanks to GPS, radioastronomy and laser telemetry, the true physical figure of the Earth – the 'geoid' – has been plotted right down to the last few millimetres. The precise location of landmarks can then be used as a basis from which to superimpose onto the geoid different map projections and geographical data.

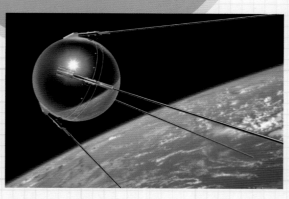

Sputnik 1, the world's first man-made satellite

An artist's impression of a satellite's field of vision as it passes over the Earth (right)

MEASURING TIME
FROM THE HOURGLASS TO
THE ATOMIC CLOCK

Ancient methods for keeping time – such as observing the Sun, clepsydras (water-clocks) and hourglasses – were supplanted by quartz oscillators during the First World War. Developed for use in sonar, these are still used in watches, computers and mobile phones. The first atomic clock appeared in 1947; this worked on the principle of forcing a quartz crystal to oscillate at a reliably constant frequency – specifically, the frequency given off by the electrons in atoms when they change energy levels; that is, when they move from an excited state to a ground state. The first truly stable atomic clocks using caesium arrived in 1955. In 1967 the International Bureau of Weights & Measures defined the second by using the transition between two energy levels of the caesium-133 atom. Accurate to one-billionth of a second or better, atomic clocks are vital to GPS; at the speed of light, one-millionth of a second translates into a distance of 300m, which is way outside an acceptable margin of error.

An atomic clock

THE RECEIVER
FROM RADIO RECEPTION
TO GPS

A GPS receiver is, first and foremost, a radio receiver, an invention of the late 19th century that has been constantly improved and miniaturised since – first with valves, then transistors, then through the introduction of integrated circuits and microelectronics. In essence, GPS links a radio receiver, which is a comparatively simple and inexpensive component, to information technology that holds in memory an image of the geoid and potentially also maps, with sufficient computing power to determine a position based on radio signals.

A Tom-Tom, a popular SatNav for cars (above)

An artist's impression of one of the 30 planned Galileo satellites (below)

THE FUTURE
COMPETITION AND
COOPERATION

GPS satellites are replaced or upgraded on a regular basis. Through successive generations, the system is set to last until at least 2030, with ever-increasing accuracy. In coming years, as it is joined by rival systems such as Galileo and Glonass, it is vital that agreements on compatibility and interchangeability are reached between competing systems to provide reliable coverage at civilian level. Such an agreement is already in place between Galileo and GPS. This evolution should bring enhanced benefits over the standard location service, such as interface with special cartographic databases and aerial photography.

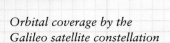

Orbital coverage by the Galileo satellite constellation

CLONING – 1996

Brave new genetic world

The first mammal to be cloned from an adult cell was a female sheep named Dolly. The process was achieved by extracting the nucleus of an ordinary cell taken from one ewe and transferring it into an egg taken from another ewe. No father, no sexual reproduction and no fertilisation of the egg by sperm was involved. Dolly's birth was a step towards the possibility of being able to 'grow' human organs for therapeutic purposes, but it also raised the spectre of unregulated cloning for 'selective breeding'.

Celebrity sheep
Dolly (above right) and one of her creators, biologist Ian Wilmut (above). Although Dolly was a major scientific breakthrough, the process that created her was rather hit-and-miss, using up around a thousand eggs taken from adult ewes. Because of this and other difficulties, cloning is still far from being a viable method of improving the productivity and quality of livestock.

Dolly the Sheep was born on 5 July, 1996, at the Roslin Institute in Edinburgh, a centre for research into animal genetics. Two British biologists were responsible for bringing her into the world: Ian Wilmut, who headed the team, and Keith Campbell. Since 1984 they had been working on a programme to breed genetically modify sheep whose milk would contain proteins that could be used in the treatment of human diseases. Their attempts to improve this technique led them to undertake experiments in cell transfer, which in turn led to reproduction through cloning.

Creating Dolly

Dolly's birth was the culmination of a highly complicated procedure. The research team began by extracting cells from the udder of a six-year-old ewe, and then isolating the nucleus of each of these cells. The nucleus contains the animal's DNA, carrying all the genetic information for inherited traits. Each nucleus

was introduced into an egg taken from another female sheep, from which the original nucleus had first been removed. The donor nucleus was fused with the receptor egg cell by means of an electrical discharge, to create an egg cell with a gene pool identical to that of the ewe from which the nucleus had been taken.

The researchers succeeded in producing 277 of these fused egg cells, then applied more electrical impulses to stimulate cell division. The developing eggs were placed in the sheep's oviducts for six days to incubate, before being retrieved. Of the 247 embryos retrieved, 29 had divided normally to the stage where the embryo forms a tiny mulberry-like structure, the 'morula', made up of 64 individual cells. These were subsequently implanted into the uterus of 13 carrier 'mother' ewes to develop normally, but only one of these ultimately produced a foetus. Eventually that foetus was born as a living lamb: Dolly.

Strictly speaking, Dolly was not the world's first cloned animal. In nature, some animal species can reproduce asexually by a process known as parthenogenesis, the simple division

In 1952 the American scientists Robert Briggs and Thomas King produced live tadpoles by introducing the nuclei of blastula cells (an early-stage embryo cell) taken from treefrogs into enucleated eggs from animals of the same species. In 1963 a Chinese researcher Tong Dizhou achieved the first true artificial cloning of an animal when he transferred the DNA of a male carp into a female's enucleated egg.

The procedure is much more complex in mammals. In 1984 the Danish scientist Steen Willadsen, working in Cambridge, was responsible for the first verified cloning of a

of a cell without the need for fertilisation of an egg. This is true of aphids, as well as some species of lizard and fishes. Yet no mammal can do this. Before Dolly, the only mammal clones were identical twins, naturally created in the womb by division of the fertilised egg.

The carp and the rabbit

The idea of cloning – the asexual reproduction of an identical copy of a living being – had fascinated scientists long before it became a possibility. In 1938 the German biologist Hans Spemann, known as the father of modern embryology, first had the idea of enucleating (that is, removing the nucleus from) frogspawn and replacing them with the nuclei of other oocytes (eggs). He chose frog's eggs because of their relatively large size. From these studies he demonstrated that each cell contains all the genetic information necessary for creating a living animal.

Cloned cat
A domestic cat cloned by the commercial enterprise 'Genetic Savings & Clone' in San Francisco: the two-year-old Mando (on the left) was the cell donor animal for the cloning of Peaches (on the right), seen here at the age of 9 months. For a fee of $50,000, the firm offers pet owners the chance to clone their animals.

Bloodstock revolution?
Prometheus (left), born in May 2003, was the world's first cloned horse and the first to be carried within its donor mother (right). These animals are the subject of an intensive ongoing study by the University of Bologna in Italy.

29

organs that would produce proteins beneficial to human health. Shortly after Dolly's birth, a transgenic cloned ewe named Polly was born, which produced milk containing a human blood-clotting factor.

The ethics of reproductive cloning

Though there is a widespread fear of things getting out of hand, the idea of human cloning remains ethically unacceptable. Even scientists take the view that the formidable technical hurdles make it not worth the risk: even supposing one knew how to do it, the success rate for cloning is never more than 5 per cent, and this would mean using the technique of ovarian puncture to extract an unfeasibly large number of eggs from women.

Fluorescent pigs
These piglets were born in 2006 to a cloned sow which had been injected with fluorescent proteins. They were living proof that clones are fertile and can transmit their genetically modified traits to the next generation.

mammal – a sheep – using nuclear transfer. The American Neil First achieved the same feat two years later with calves, while a team led by Jean-Paul Renard in France successfully cloned rabbits using this technique in 2002.

However, all of these animals came from embryonic cells. The truly revolutionary thing about Dolly's birth was that she was the first mammal to be cloned from an adult somatic cell. This achievement sparked a passionate debate, for and against. Critics claimed that it opened the door to eugenics and to armies of cloned human beings. But in truth, the objectives of animal cloning are far less sinister and more pragmatic: to improve livestock pedigree and to develop genetically modified animal

Cloning milestones
In 1997 scientists at the Oregon Regional Primate Research Center in the USA created two rhesus monkeys, Neti and Ditto (below), from DNA taken from cells of developing monkey embryos.

PUTTING IT INTO PERSPECTIVE

Due to its high failure rate, cloning cannot yet compete with traditional methods of selective breeding for improving the pedigree of livestock animals. Moreover, producing a clone is a very expensive business – around £9,000 for a calf, for example. On the other hand, cloning is already proving useful in other ways. It can help to stabilise certain traits in particular strains of animal noted for the quality of their milk or meat, for example, or as exceptional breeding stock. It can also be used to save species that are threatened with extinction and, by teaming it with transgenic techniques, it can help to create stable strains of transgenic animals that produce therapeutic proteins in their milk or blood for use by human patients. Transgenic animals have already yielded valuable proteins to cure clotting disorders such as haemophilia and to create vital antibodies such as immunoglobulin.

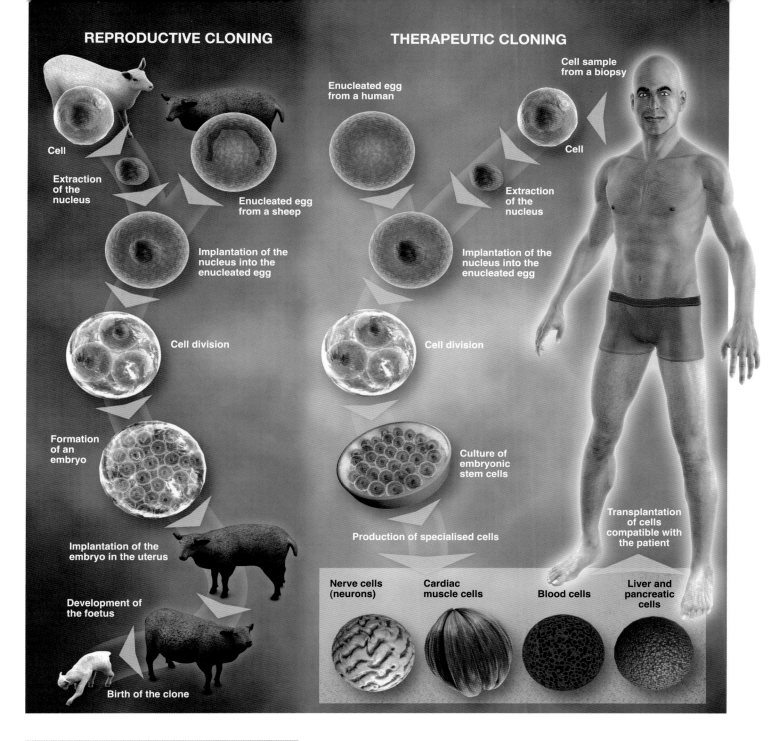

REPRODUCTIVE CLONING

Cell

Extraction of the nucleus

Enucleated egg from a sheep

Implantation of the nucleus into the enucleated egg

Cell division

Formation of an embryo

Implantation of the embryo in the uterus

Development of the foetus

Birth of the clone

THERAPEUTIC CLONING

Enucleated egg from a human

Cell sample from a biopsy

Cell

Extraction of the nucleus

Implantation of the nucleus into the enucleated egg

Cell division

Culture of embryonic stem cells

Transplantation of cells compatible with the patient

Production of specialised cells

Nerve cells (neurons)	Cardiac muscle cells	Blood cells	Liver and pancreatic cells

MORE MISS THAN HIT

While it is possible to run off an infinite number of photocopies from a single original document, the same is not true of animal cloning. No fewer than 433 attempts at nuclear transfer, of which 277 were successful, were made to create Dolly. And despite intensive ongoing research, among bovine species the number of live offspring is never more than 20 per cent of the embryos transferred to the host mother. This low success rate is even worse in other species: just 8 live births for every 100 sheep embryos, 5 per cent in pigs and goats, and under 1 per cent in most other species.

The question became even more pressing and sensitive in 1998, when two American teams led by James Thomson and John Gearheart managed for the first time to cultivate stem cells taken from human embryos. These embryonic stem cells could be used to generate every kind of tissue within the organism. In embryos 5–6 days old, they formed a small cluster that in time would develop into the future child, while other cells went to form the placenta. By combining the technique of cloning by nuclear transfer and the cultivation of stem cells, it became theoretically feasible to produce from any given individual human embryo a reservoir of stem cells that could be 'farmed' to produce cells or tissue to combat

The two types of cloning
Reproductive cloning is geared towards creating an entire animal, whereas therapeutic cloning is designed to produce stem cells for medical research.

diseases or replace a failing organ, without any danger of immune rejection by the host. This development raised hopes of a whole new branch of regenerative medicine.

Before further development could take place, legal and ethical safeguards had to be put in place to protect against the dual menace of reproductive cloning and 'objectification' of the human embryo. All the more so since the dividing line between therapeutic and reproductive cloning was so thin: the process is exactly the same, at least at the outset, but instead of arresting the development of the embryo, as is the case when harvesting stem cells, it is theoretically possible to let it continue and then reimplant the embryo into the womb of the carrier mother.

Although legislative measures varied from country to country, almost all explicitly banned reproductive cloning. Some, like Germany, quickly enacted laws that prohibited all forms

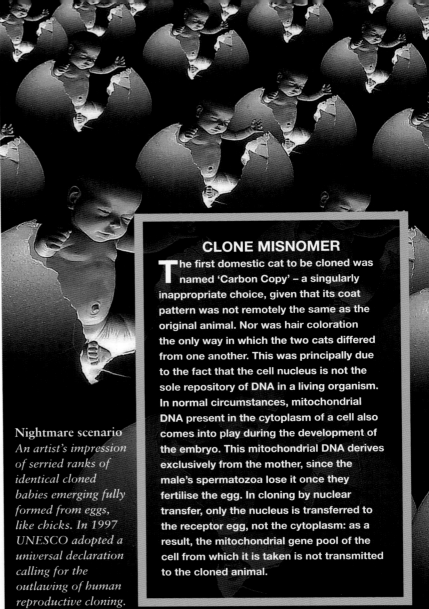

Nightmare scenario
An artist's impression of serried ranks of identical cloned babies emerging fully formed from eggs, like chicks. In 1997 UNESCO adopted a universal declaration calling for the outlawing of human reproductive cloning.

CLONE MISNOMER

The first domestic cat to be cloned was named 'Carbon Copy' – a singularly inappropriate choice, given that its coat pattern was not remotely the same as the original animal. Nor was hair coloration the only way in which the two cats differed from one another. This was principally due to the fact that the cell nucleus is not the sole repository of DNA in a living organism. In normal circumstances, mitochondrial DNA present in the cytoplasm of a cell also comes into play during the development of the embryo. This mitochondrial DNA derives exclusively from the mother, since the male's spermatozoa lose it once they fertilise the egg. In cloning by nuclear transfer, only the nucleus is transferred to the receptor egg, not the cytoplasm: as a result, the mitochondrial gene pool of the cell from which it is taken is not transmitted to the cloned animal.

Human farm
In a scene from the 2004 science-fiction film The Island, *directed by Michael Bay, clones are being 'grown' in a laboratory for the benefit of billionaires able to pay for cosmetic genetic surgery or for organs to be created for a vital transplant. In the film, two of the clones rebel against this exploitation.*

of cloning. Therapeutic cloning is also illegal in France and Italy, but is allowed in Britain, Belgium, the Netherlands, Australia, South Korea and the state of California in the USA.

An outmoded technique?

In February 2004, and again in March of the following year, the South Korean researcher Dr Hwang Woo-suk reported that he had succeeded in creating human embryonic stem cells by cloning them. Yet all attempts to reproduce the results obtained by the Korean team failed. In December 2005 Hwang was forced to admit that he had falsified his findings. The fiasco was a bitter setback for all embryologists and biotechnicians engaged in research on therapeutic cloning.

A few months later, in August 2006, two Japanese scientists, Shinya Yamanaka and Kazutoshi Takahashi, became the first to reprogramme the skin cells of adult mice by injecting into them four genes that basically

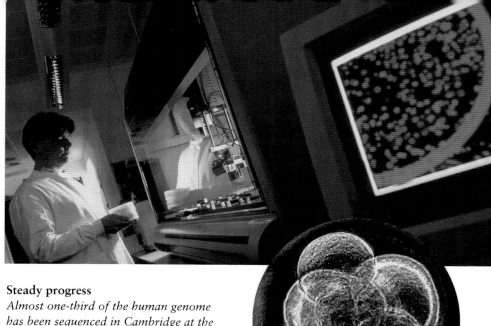

Steady progress
Almost one-third of the human genome has been sequenced in Cambridge at the Sanger Molecular Biology Laboratory (above), named after Frederick Sanger.

caused the skin cells to revert to the state of embryonic stem cells. Their results were corroborated in 2007 by two American research teams. Since then, it has become possible to produce human stem cells – or iPS cells, as they are known ('induced pluripotent stem cells') – by a similar method, without having to get involved in cloning and its highly charged ethical arguments.

In common with many of his colleagues, Ian Wilmut, co-creator of Dolly, renounced nuclear transfer in favour of reprogramming, which is more productive and socially more acceptable. The first successful human cloning took place in 2008, when a Californian research team fused skin cell nuclei and human eggs to produce three human embryos, which took six days to develop. The achievement passed virtually unnoticed.

Historic breakthrough
The world's first cloned human embryo – seen here (above) three days after the nuclear transfer took place – was created in May 2005 by a team led by Dr Miodrag Stojkovic at the Centre for Life in Newcastle upon Tyne. The cluster of cells, known as a blastocyst, was made by inserting DNA into an unfertilised human egg and inducing it to multiply.

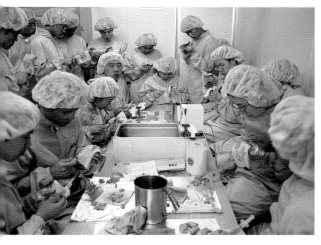

Wasted time and effort
The stem-cell research team of Dr Hwang Woo-suk in Seoul, South Korea (above). Having fabricated results, in October 2009 Hwang was sentenced to two years in prison for embezzling public funds and contravening bioethical legislation.

VENTER'S VENTURE

On 21 May, 2010, the American gene entrepreneur Craig Venter announced in the journal *Science* that he had created the first synthetic living cell. Venter stated that it had been 'totally derived from a synthetic chromosome, made with four bottles of chemicals on a chemical synthesiser, starting with information in a computer'. The genome was an exact copy of that of the bacterium *Mycoplasma mycoides*, whose four DNA bases (ACGT) were contained in the bottles in Venter's lab. Once this genome had been constructed, it was inserted into a natural bacterium whose genome had been removed. The success of the operation was confirmed by the fact that a colony of *M. mycoides* formed within the Petri dish. The way now seemed open to modifying living organisms at the cellular level, an extraordinary challenge that also points the way forward not only to new medical treatments but also to the potential creation of hitherto unknown species.

Access from all areas

In the 1990s, information and communications technology (ICT) suddenly transformed the world of work, enabling many people to work as efficiently from home as in the office, potentially saving themselves the drudgery of commuting and reducing rush-hour congestion. Internet access and a mobile phone gave everyone the opportunity of working remotely from the office or place of learning.

For years remote working or 'telecommuting' – the term was first coined as far back as the 1950s – remained a marginal activity for the few, despite the advent of the fax and the personal computer. Yet by the beginning of the new millennium this new way of working was in full swing thanks to the giant leaps taken in ICT. New hardware and software, such as 3G connectivity, instant messaging, webcams, teleconferencing, Skype networks and intranet facilities, made distance an irrelevance, putting remote workers instantly in touch with the office from wherever they happened to be. Shared agendas, exchange platforms and groupware enabled user groups to collaborate at long distance on the same project.

Logging in

Nowadays, the world of work is no longer defined by a set time or place. Remote working (sometimes called 'e-working') has made the boundary between the professional and personal spheres more flexible than ever before.

Crossing continents

From a desk in their head office in Chicago, two managers of an international company hold a teleconference with colleagues in Atlanta (Georgia) and London. Virtual meetings like this save companies the expense of many unnecessary business trips abroad.

Today, almost 25 per cent of employees in the United States and Canada (7 per cent of them in the public services) work remotely in some form; in Japan the figure is 20 per cent. The average in the European Union lags behind at 13 per cent, though this statistic covers a wide disparity between nations that have embraced the practice, such as in Scandinavia and the Benelux countries (15 per cent of employees), and those that have not, such as Britain and France (about 7 per cent). This discrepancy is explained both by the degree of political support in different countries for such an initiative (through tax incentives to employers, for instance) and by the reluctance of individual firms to embrace new methods.

A multifaceted phenomenon

In 2002 the European Union defined telecommuting as: 'a form of organising and/ or performing work, using information technology, in the context of an employment contract/relationship, where work, which could also be performed at the employers' premises, is carried out away from those premises on a regular basis.' The definition was deliberately broad to include various types of remote worker, from a salaried employee

SETTING THE STANDARD

In 2002 the European Union drew up a framework agreement on teleworking, with a view to defining the legal status of remote-working salaried staff. Written into law in all 27 member states, this directive established the principles of voluntary participation, by which no-one can be forced to telework, and mutual reversibility, which means either the employee or the employer can terminate the arrangement whenever they wish. Remote workers have the same rights and legal benefits as other employees, with no greater workload imposed upon them than on in-house colleagues. Employers agreed to respect employees' private lives, with rules on when and how they can be contacted at home.

working from home to a freelancer running his or her own operation. Likewise, remote working takes many different forms.

• **Teleworking from home** is the most familiar scenario. It is undertaken from a person's house, either full-time or, often in the case of salaried employees, part-time interspersed with regular attendance at the office. It is ideal for freelancers, who cover a wide spectrum of occupations, from people doing e-commerce to designers and editors working on behalf of publishing companies.

Work on the move

All international airports now have zones where travellers can get free Wi-Fi connection to access the Internet and their e-mail accounts. This facility (right) is at Kastrup in Denmark. Between 2007 and the end of 2009, the number of Danes regularly working from home rose from a quarter to almost a third of the total workforce, placing Denmark at the forefront of teleworking in Europe.

• **Teleworking on the move** is a boon to all those employees whose jobs require them to be absent from the office on a regular basis, such as engineers, maintenance technicians and sales reps. With the right equipment, they can now log in to their work station from practically anywhere – hotel rooms, while flying or travelling on high-speed trains, or from their clients' offices.

• **Satellite offices:** more and more firms today are outsourcing so-called 'back-office'

Reducing stress
Far from the hurly-[...] the trading floor, th[...] commodities trader [...] uses multiple screen[...] fast Internet connec[...] follow the markets, [...] financial advice, and [...] and sell shares – all [...] comfort and relative [...] of his home.

WORK IN A WIRELESS AIRPORT

Outsourcing

The development of satellite offices, like this one (above) located in a Parisian suburb, was based on a distinction between 'front-office' operations involving face-to-face contact with clients that had to be conducted in-house, and ancillary 'back-office' tasks.

operations – such as secretarial support, accounting, data capture and logistics – to facilities connected to the head office but located outside of the main urban centres. The move can generate huge savings, given the high cost of office rents in big cities.

• **Telework centres** are an alternative to working from home or the satellite office. These cybercafé-like spaces dedicated to teleworking bring together under one roof freelancers and outworking employees from different enterprises. Sited in rural locations, they are often supported by local authorities as a way of revitalising their region. In 2009 Australia set up 100 such centres in the most economically depressed areas of the country.

Pros and cons

Remote working offers a number of distinct advantages, both for the individual worker and for the employer/client. For a start, it allows people to achieve a better balance between their working and home lives, reducing stress as it saves them hours on the daily commute and saving them money on transport, food and often child-minding. It also enables people to decamp from the city to the countryside if they wish and improve their quality of life. Working from home saves freelancers the expense of renting an office. Studies have shown that teleworking helps reduce burn-out and stress, and by giving people a new sense of autonomy and self-worth it also increases productivity.

'Your call is important to us …'
Workers at a call-centre for an American multinational, based in a suburb of New Delhi (above). Outsourcing call centres to countries like India can save company's money in lower wage costs, but often comes at a price paid in reduced customer satisfaction.

Nevertheless it is not the ideal solution for everyone; if someone is disorganised or lacks self-discipline, the separation between private and professional life can become dangerously blurred.

One great benefit for employers is that teleworking enables them to cut down on office space and so reduce costs. Several large companies have already cottoned-on to this fact: for example, by having 12 per cent of its workforce operating out of house, British Telecom has saved more than £200 million in office rental over 10 years. In addition, teleworking enables employers to assess workers' performance by results, rather than simply requiring them to turn up at an office for a given number of hours. On the other hand, employers do need to keep in regular contact with their outworkers, especially where collaborative team projects are concerned. This new world of work is based on mutual trust and increasingly firms are willing to relinquish direct day-to-day control over their employees.

Online education

Like teleworking, ICT-based learning is also gaining ground fast. E-learning embraces a wide range of people, including people in work, those seeking employment or wishing to retrain, and students working towards a degree. It has proved particularly useful in the case of primary or secondary school pupils who, for family reasons, have to take their lessons from home. The Internet allows them to download coursework and videos, to access digitised databases, to experience real-time tuition, liaise directly with the teacher, and (via online forum discussions with other students) to assess their own progress. This method of interactive education offers distinct advantages in teaching pupils or students how to organise their time, saving them the time and cost of travel, and making them feel that they are playing an active role in their own education. Its main drawback is the lack of face-to-face contact with teachers, a real problem if a student encounters difficulties. This is why periodic meetings in person are factored in to most distance-learning programmes.

The early 21st century has seen a gradual erosion of the technological obstacles that once hampered the growth of telecommuting and distance learning. The steep rise in energy costs and, paradoxically, the global economic crisis have further contributed to the growth of both, by bringing the advantages into focus for employers and employees alike.

Virtual lecture
In an auditorium that normally plays host to magistrates' hearings, medical students from the University of Grenoble undertake coursework via DVD. The high number of enrolments on the first year of the course made this provision necessary.

The Tamagotchi 1996

Developed by the Japanese toy designer Aki Maita and marketed from November 1996 onwards by her employer, the Bandai company, the Tamagotchi was the world's first interactive robot toy. The concept grew from the idea of replacing traditional pets – which were too much of a nuisance to look after in tiny Japanese apartments – by virtual creatures. At the same time, though, owners were required to take on the responsibility of adoption.

Equipped with a small LCD display and managed by a simple programme, each Tamagotchi simulated a digital pet housed inside a plastic egg-shaped casing. Three buttons allowed the user to select and carry out daily tasks, such as feeding, cleaning and grooming. If these were carried out scrupulously, the Tamagotchi would happily continue to function; conversely, if it was neglected it would emit shrill noises to alert its owner. If its owner failed to respond, it died. Or, to be more precise, the Tamagotchi went back to its own planet, and the player had to start all over again. Some fans even went so far as to create virtual cemeteries for their 'dead' Tamagotchis.

Followers of fashion
Tamagotchis come in a huge variety of patterns, including a camouflaged version (top right) and a flowery one (above). The manufacturer Bandai has created a special website dedicated to its product, called 'Tamagotchi Town'.

A global craze

Within a year, Tamagotchis had spread to 30 or so countries around the world, generating masses of spin-off merchandise – clothing, cuddly toys, stationery, even apps for mobile phones, giving users a permanent interface for play. By 2004 an infrared connection between 'male' and 'female' Tamagotchis enabled these small digital pets to communicate with one another, marry and produce offspring. As of 2010, some 76 million had been sold worldwide.

THE 'MUST HAVE' FURBY

In 1998, after two years of development, the Americans Dave Hampton and Caleb Chung launched their revolutionary interactive robotic toy, the Furby (right), at the American International Toy Fair. This animated cuddly toy is fitted with sensors that enable it to hear sounds, to tell whether it is being touched and to perceive light. It also had a voice-emitting function that could produce pre-programmed words or phrases (in the Furbish language); the more they were petted, the more they said. Electric motors opened and closed the eyes and moved the ears. Later models were fitted with voice-recognition and could perform more complex facial movements. Furbies were a runaway success: to date more than 40 million have been sold around the world.

E-COMMERCE – 1996
Shopping with a mouse

When e-commerce first started up in 1996, it was on a modest scale. But those in the know had no doubt that it was the start of a new market with huge growth potential. Both for inter-company trade ('business to business', or B2B) and for selling goods to end users ('business to consumer', or B2C) the rapid rise in Internet usage has transformed the retail landscape beyond all recognition.

The beginnings of e-commerce were a long way from earth-shattering. 'World Avenue', a virtual store launched by IBM on 13 August, 1996, was wound up after less than a year online due to lack of visitors. And other sites fared little better: the performance of MCI Communication's 'I-commerce' site was distinctly underwhelming, while the webmall 'e-Christmas', a joint venture by Microsoft, Hewlett-Packard and the logistics company UPS, recorded only around 500 transactions between its inception on 10 November, 1997, and 8 January, 1998.

Yet despite the unpromising start, online business gradually started to pick up. Sales began to climb from 1999 onwards and as now-familiar companies and sites such as Amazon and eBay expanded, it became possible for consumers to shop from the four corners of the Earth without leaving their homes. Before long it was possible to buy anything at any hour of the day or night, from goods of all kinds – books, records, films, wine, groceries – to services such as train and flight reservations or hotel rooms.

Negligible costs

To set up in electronic commerce, vendors simply create a site advertising their products or services. Publicity is drummed up by posting advertisements on search engines and in the press. The shopping customer fills a 'virtual' shopping basket on the strength of a description and photographs of the product. While it is obviously not possible to touch or smell the goods in question, or talk to a real salesperson, one benefit for the buyer is that it is possible to easily compare prices for the same item from a host of different sellers.

On the Internet, many of the overheads associated with traditional points of sale – such as renting a shop, paying the wages of shop staff, warehousing and local business tax – no longer apply. Stock can remain with the manufacturer until ordered (unless the manufacturer sets up their own direct-selling operation). The only cost attached to the factory-gate price of goods is transport, and even this only relates to material products: software, music and films can be downloaded by the end-user once they have paid for usage, without any physical goods changing hands.

Retail revolution
Security and visibility are the two watchwords for success in selling via the Internet. The world's leading online auction site, eBay, uses the secure PayPal money-transfer system to enable customers to pay for the goods they have successfully bid for. In 2006 eBay gave Google, the world's top search engine, exclusive rights to post its sponsored links.

ETHICALLY RESPONSIBLE E-SHOPPING?

Could shopping online help to save the planet? A study conducted in 2009 by an agency specialising in questions of energy consumption and the environment certainly seems to indicate that this might be so. Comparing the carbon footprint of 5,400 deliveries of goods ordered through the Internet with the corresponding impact of the same products bought through a traditional retail distribution network, it concluded that the e-commerce mode of shopping shaved 53,000km off the total distance travelled by the goods, or an average of 10km per order. By cutting the distance that goods have to travel, it stands to reason that cybercommerce generates less carbon and greenhouse gases.

Delivering the goods
One of the huge logistics facilities belonging to the world's leading online retailer, Amazon (above). In this 46,000m² warehouse, two shifts of employees work from early morning to 8.30 at night, six days a week, making up packages to send out to customers.

Job creation
E-commerce can help to generate new work. This young entrepreneur in Lagos, Nigeria (inset above), has set himself up as a middleman processing online orders for people with no computer access.

Competition and innovation

As competition for online sales intensified, online buyers showed they could be extremely fickle, shopping around in search of a bargain. One way that online retailers seek to gain a loyalty advantage is to develop personalised relations with their customers, building up a profile of their buying habits. This kind of marketing tool is just one of the ways in which some companies have successfully exploited the potential of e-commerce. The American-originated site Amazon.com is the most famous example. As early as 1999, this virtual bookshop had a catalogue of 3.1 million titles and a customer base of 4.5 million potential buyers. It then diversified into non-English language books, followed by CDs, videos, electronic goods and more.

Bursting the dot.com bubble

As the 21st century dawned, the future of the Web-based economy looked rosy. Venture capitalists were investing huge sums in start-up costs for online businesses. But then, in March 2000, the so-called 'Internet bubble' burst and one after another, 'dot.com' companies failed.

CYBERPIRATES AHOY!

One technique used by fraudsters to try to obtain the bank details of online shoppers is so-called 'phishing'. This involves sending a bogus e-mail to the target, claiming to be from a familiar and trusted site – possibly the customer's own bank. The addressee is asked to click on a link in the message, which sends them to a fake website mimicking a genuine site, which downloads their details. Almost all genuine Internet sales sites have sophisticated security systems, and can be recognised by their URL and/or a padlock symbol at the top of bottom or the screen.

and away the main products sold on line; food-shopping is one of the few sectors where e-commerce has not yet eclipsed traditional sales. Nor are buyers averse to spending serious sums of money on the Web, with many people making purchases of big items such as luxury cars and jewellery. Most people still pay by debit or credit card, although PayPal is growing in popularity, especially on sites like eBay. PayPal acts as an intermediary between the vendor and the buyer, automatically and instantly transferring the requisite sum from a bank account designated by the customer.

On the flip side, delays in delivery are not uncommon and price-comparison sites are not always entirely reliable. Another problem is that some service providers are quick to take the money from customers' accounts, but not so prompt in delivering the goods.

THE UPWARD ONLINE TREND

In October 2011, a report from the Office of National Statistics showed that online spending in the UK had reached £1 in every £10. This represented a rise of 30 per cent since the same time the previous year.

Yet just a decade after this mighty crash, one-and-a-half billion people are connected to the Internet and e-commerce has proven its enormous potential. Thousands of on-line sales sites are now attempting to emulate the success of the likes of Amazon, Yahoo! and eBay. Some companies, such as the computer manufacturer Dell, who operate purely on the Web, while other sites have been developed by traditional retailers who now feel the need to have a presence on the Web. Today, cost-effective software encourages even the smallest of entrepreneurs to try their hand at e-commerce.

A world of online shoppers

The UK takes the lead among European nations in terms of e-commerce, with online sales in 2009 amounting to 42.7 billion euros (approaching £40 billion), followed by Germany (33.4 billion euros) and France (24.7 billion euros). Together, these three countries account for some 70 per cent of all online transactions in Europe. High-tech goods, books, travel, and clothing are far

Safe and secure
A major factor in the growth of online shopping has been the development of secure payment methods, reassuring customers that their bank or credit card details will not be hijacked by hackers.

Delivered to your door
Most online transactions are fast and efficient, with goods ordered on the Web one day arriving at the customer's door by courier service the next.

Unlocking the mysteries of the universe

Scientists have been sending probes out into space for the past 50 years and have been rewarded with almost miraculous images sent back with other data to Earth. From the blue face of the planet Neptune to the battered profiles of asteroids to the beauty of a sunrise on Mars, they have revealed to us stunning, surprising and at times unsettling images of our Solar System.

Pioneering probe
A computer-generated artwork of the unmanned Soviet probe Luna I *orbiting the Moon in 1959 (below). The probe's flight to reach the Moon lasted 34 hours. Its discoveries included the absence of a lunar magnetic field and the presence of a solar wind.*

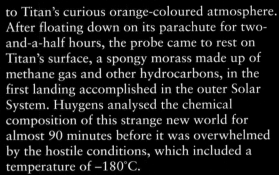
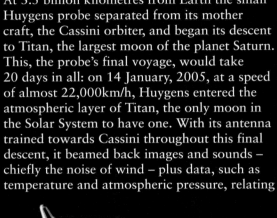

At 3.5 billion kilometres from Earth the small Huygens probe separated from its mother craft, the Cassini orbiter, and began its descent to Titan, the largest moon of the planet Saturn. This, the probe's final voyage, would take 20 days in all: on 14 January, 2005, at a speed of almost 22,000km/h, Huygens entered the atmospheric layer of Titan, the only moon in the Solar System to have one. With its antenna trained towards Cassini throughout this final descent, it beamed back images and sounds – chiefly the noise of wind – plus data, such as temperature and atmospheric pressure, relating to Titan's curious orange-coloured atmosphere. After floating down on its parachute for two-and-a-half hours, the probe came to rest on Titan's surface, a spongy morass made up of methane gas and other hydrocarbons, in the first landing accomplished in the outer Solar System. Huygens analysed the chemical composition of this strange new world for almost 90 minutes before it was overwhelmed by the hostile conditions, which included a temperature of –180°C.

Cassini is still conducting flybys of Saturn, taking photographs of the planet, its rings and its other moons. The scientists in charge of the programme, from NASA and the European Space Agency (ESA), are debating how to bring the orbiter's mission to an end, weighing up the pros and cons of having it plunge through the rings to collide with Saturn's atmosphere, or sending it down onto Titan. The question has still not been decided.

Probes to the Moon

The very first probes to be launched were designed to investigate our own Moon. These missions began with the American Pioneer 4 and the Soviet Luna 2, both in 1959, which sent back the first images of the dark side of the Moon. At the time, the Space Race between the two superpowers was just getting underway. The intense rivalry generated would culminate in the Americans putting astronauts on the Moon ten years later, but it also spawned a whole host of other successful space exploration missions – not least through the great leaps forward that were made in rocket technology throughout the 1960s. In 1966 the USSR pulled off the first successful landing of a probe in the Solar System: on 3 February that year, Luna 9 touched down on the Moon and sent back stunning panoramic views of its surface.

Amazing clarity
The Mars Reconnaissance Orbiter (MRO) satellite went into orbit around the planet in March 2006. Since then, high-resolution imaging equipment on board MRS has sent back pin-sharp images of features of the planet's surface, such as this impact crater near the equator.

MARTIAN ROVERS

Exploration rovers have been roaming the surface of Mars since 1997, defying all predictions about their operational lifespan, originally set at just 6 months. The identical twin rovers *Opportunity* and *Spirit*, despatched to Mars in 2003, are among NASA's most remarkable success stories. Measuring just 1.5m in height, 2.3m across and 1.6m long, they are fitted with six wheels each and are powered by solar panels. Packed with scientific instruments and equipped with cameras and robot arms for taking soil samples, they were designed to study Martian geology and to find proof of whether water – and hence life – could ever have been present on the planet. *Spirit* travelled almost 8km before getting bogged down in sand in 2009; even so, it continued to send back data on its surroundings till 2010. *Opportunity* has covered 33.5km and is still going strong.

More than 80 missions have been devoted to the Earth's Moon, making it the most probed celestial body bar none. One of the most recent was LCROSS, the Lunar CRater Observation and Sensing Satellite, launched in June 2009. In October 2009 it was deliberately crash-landed into the Crabeus crater not far from the Moon's south pole. While examining and analysing the plume of dust caused by the impact, astrophysicists were able to detect the presence of water in the form of ice crystals. It now seems certain that our Moon has large quantities of water trapped under a layer of grey dust at the base of certain craters that never see sunlight.

Missions to Mars

At 220 million kilometres from the Sun, Mars is the second most popular target for space probes, with 40 missions clocked up to date. In 1965 NASA's Mariner 4 flew by the Red Planet for the first time, discovering in the process the presence of a thin atmosphere mainly comprised of carbon dioxide. Then, on 20 July, 1976, the American Viking probe landed on Mars and took the first photos of the surface. That same year, on 3 September, it was joined by Viking 2. These twin probes analysed the composition of the soil and searched, in vain, for evidence of primitive life forms. The exploration of Mars by space

probes has not been free from disasters – in fact, almost half of all missions to Mars have ended in failure. The Soviet probe Phobos 1 was lost in 1988. Five years later contact with NASA's Mars Observer was lost some months after it went into orbit. In 2003 Beagle 2 crashed into the planet's surface. Such events served only to deepen the sense of mystery that surrounds our neighbouring planet.

But other Mars missions have been a resounding success. On 6 July, 1997, the

Movement on Mars
A partial panoramic image taken by the navigation camera on board the Mars Exploration Rover, Opportunity. The solar panels of the lander are visible in the foreground, with tracks beyond made by the rover.

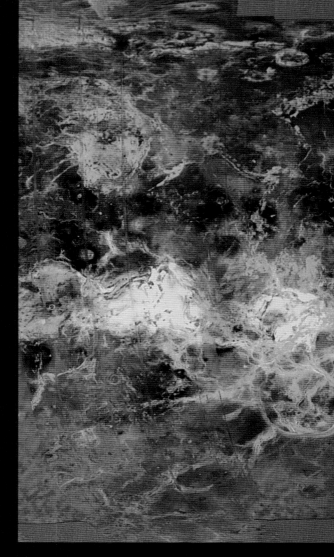

Forbidding planet
A radar map of part of the surface of Venus (right), created in 1991 from data gathered by the Magellan space probe. Placed in orbit above Venus by the space shuttle Atlantis *in 1989, Magellan made a 1:500,000 scale map of the fiery planet showing the presence of thousands of volcanoes.*

Investigating deep space
A model of the Pioneer 10 probe, launched from Cape Kennedy in 1972. It carried on board a plaque with data about the human race for any extra-terrestrial life form that might find it.

Sojourner rover, carried there on board the Mars Pathfinder probe, became the first vehicle ever to explore the planet's surface. *Sojourner*'s primary tasks were to study the atmosphere and take soil samples. This was the first of a series of Mars rovers; seven years later, *Opportunity* and *Spirit* added to the growing bank of data obtained on the planet's geology, atmosphere and climate. Results from the Mars Reconnaissance Orbiter Project in 2011 even suggest that water in liquid form may flow on the planet's surface during its summer.

Venus – a raging inferno

In 1967 a key moment came in the exploration of Venus, the Earth's nearest planetary neighbour at 108 million kilometres away. The venture had begun five years earlier when

THE PIONEER ANOMALY

The interplanetary probes Pioneer 10 and 11, launched in 1972 and 1973, are by now more than 10 billion kilometres from Earth, far beyond the bounds of our Solar System. Along with Voyager 1 and 2, they have ventured deeper into space than any other man-made objects. Contact with Pioneer 11 was lost in 1995 and Pioneer 10 went in 2003, but prior to this the positional data beamed back by the probes gave rise to one of the great mysteries of modern physics. It transpired that the probes were behind schedule on their flight plan, as though they were being held back by some mysterious force. Scientists speculated on the cause, but failed to come up with a conclusive answer. The two probes had both slowed down by precisely the same degree, which ruled out any technical malfunction. Moreover, they were located at opposite poles of our Solar System. The scientists concluded provisionally that the phenomenon called into question the very laws of gravity. Some experts believe that the so-called 'Pioneer Anomaly' may indicate that the laws of gravitational physics, which state that all objects are affected in the same way by gravity, do not apply in deep space.

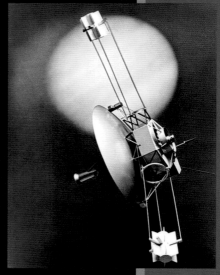

the American Mariner 2 spacecraft achieved a flyby. This was now surpassed as the Soviet probe Venera 4 landed on the planet's surface. The probe's investigations revealed a temperature of around 250°C and atmospheric pressures between 15 and 22 times greater than those on Earth. This extreme environment is the result of the thick, acrid atmosphere of carbon dioxide that envelops Venus.

The planet that has been dubbed Earth's 'evil twin', being the closest both in size and position relative to the Sun, fascinates astronomers. In theory, it should be able to support life, but instead it is a raging furnace. The last mission to be sent to Venus, the ESA's Venus Express launched in 2005, orbited for 486 days, studying the greenhouse effect created by its atmosphere. Gaining a better awareness of how CO_2 build-up contributes to temperature rise on the planet's surface will help in efforts to understand and combat what is happening to our own planet.

To Jupiter and beyond

Moving beyond the inner planets and the asteroid belt to the outer reaches of our Solar System, the first planet to be encountered by

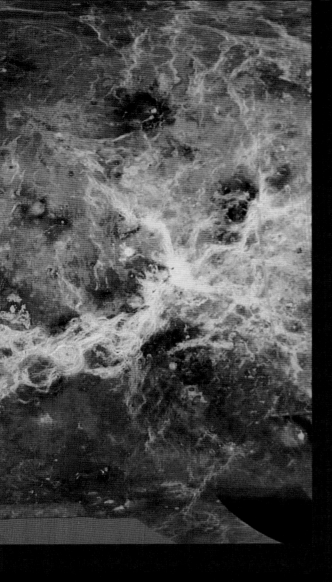

THE ART OF PRECISION AIMING

anding a probe on a comet – one of the millions of asteroids that
fly through space between Mars and Jupiter – involves hitting a
target just a few hundred kilometres across after a journey of literally
millions of kilometres. These celestial bodies are of particular interest
to astrophysicists, as they comprise the raw material from which all the
planets were formed. In 1985 the NASA probe Ice was the first to cross
the tail of a comet (Giacobini–Zinner); the following year it passed close
to Halley's comet, as this in turn was approaching the Sun. Twenty years
later, NASA's Stardust collected particles from deep within the tail of
the 'Wild 2' comet and brought the samples back to Earth. In 2005 the
Japanese probe Hayabusa attained orbit around the asteroid Itokawa in
order to study the chemical make-up of its surface. The same year,
Deep Impact released an impactor onto the comet Tempel 1 to examine
the composition of its interior through the plume of debris kicked up.
The European Space Agency's Rosetta probe, planned for launch in
2014, will be the first to land on the surface of a comet. They are aiming
for comet Churyumov–Gerasimenko, which is just 4km in diameter.

deep-space probes was Jupiter, at a distance of
780 million kilometres from Earth. The first
spacecraft to fly past Jupiter was Pioneer 10,
in December 1973, followed shortly after by its
twin Pioneer 11. These probes studied Jupiter's
very deep atmosphere and sent back stunning
photographs of the planet itself and also of
some of its moons. Later, other probes destined
for more distant planets flew past Jupiter: in

Eruptions in space
*An image taken
by* Voyager 1 *on
5 March, 1979,
shows a volcanic
plume on Io, one
of the moons of
Jupiter (below).
Some 150 active
volcanoes have
now been identified
on Io.*

Jupiter's companions
*A composite image from
photographs taken by*
Voyager 1 *shows Jupiter with
its four Galilean moons.
Io (upper right) is closest to
Jupiter, followed by Europa,
Ganymede, then Callisto.*

Studying Saturn
An artist's impression of the Cassini–Huygens probe during the Saturn Orbit Insertion (SOI) manoeuvre (top). On 25 December, 2004, the Huygens module detached from its mother craft and proceeded to photograph satellites of the main planet, such as the icy moon Dione, more than 300,000km away from the planet's rings. This image of Dione was taken in October 2005 (above right).

ROBOTS REPLACE HUMANS

Aside from the crews of the International Space Station (ISS), no humans have ventured into space since the Apollo missions to the Moon from 1969 to 1972. Astronauts from the USA and the cosmonauts of the USSR have been supplanted by robots. The chief reason for this is the huge cost of manned missions, but in addition automatic probes are ideal for collecting samples and photographs. The downside is that they cannot improvise if problems arise. The continuing fascination for the Apollo programme shows that manned spaceflight is still a powerful symbol and a milestone in the history of human achievement. Both China and India are planning missions to the Moon by 2020, again as a symbol of national progress.

1979, while en route to Saturn, Voyager 2 discovered active volcanoes on Io, one of the moons of Jupiter. This spectacular sighting was the first time that volcanic eruptions had been observed anywhere other than on Earth. Jupiter is the sole focus of NASA's Juno mission, planned for 2016. One of the main objectives will be to find out what causes the auroras that play around the planet's poles.

To the frontiers of the Solar System

In 1979, long before Cassini–Huygens, Saturn yielded up some of its secrets for the first time when Pioneer 11 flew past it. This probe captured amazing images of Saturn's rings and studied the movements of the layers of gas that make up the planet's atmosphere. Voyagers 1 and 2 performed flybys of Saturn in 1980 and

1981 and these revealed three new satellites: Atlas, Prometheus and Pandora. The images taken by the Voyager probes later led to the discovery of five further satellites.

In 1985 Voyager 2 arrived in the vicinity of Uranus, some 3 billion kilometres from the Sun. Astronomers were excited by the news: even the most powerful telescopes had never been able to show the extraordinary blue-green face of the planet, produced by the methane gas of its atmosphere. The photographs taken by Voyager 2 revealed ten new satellites of Uranus. Then, in 1989, Voyager 2 approached Neptune. Again, the data it produced was astonishing, showing the planet to be a deep blue colour, with an immense spot of an even

Methane moon
An infrared image of the atmosphere of Saturn's largest moon, Titan (right), taken by the Cassini spacecraft in 2004. Much of Titan's atmosphere is methane and it is ten times denser than Earth's atmosphere.

MERCURY AND THE SUN

The main problem in using probes to investigate the Sun and its nearest planet, Mercury, is not just the intense heat but also the damaging radiation given off by the Sun. Few probes could withstand this punishment. Ulysses, a joint NASA–ESA project, was the first craft to fly past the Sun in 1995. Its mission was to study the heliosphere, the vast area around the Sun that is the source of the solar wind. In 1974 the Mariner 10 probe was the first to fly past Mercury and take photographs of the surface. This planet, the smallest in the Solar System, became the subject of major attention in 2011 when Messenger went into orbit around it, the first craft to do so. The main focus of attention will be the mysterious magnetic field that surrounds Mercury, which no theoretical modelling has yet been able to explain successfully.

Moonscape
The surface of Titan (right), as viewed from a distance of 5km and photographed by ESA's Huygens probe during its descent on 14 January, 2005.

Closest to the Sun
A false-colour image of Mercury's cratered surface (below), taken in January 2008 by the Messenger spacecraft. In the centre is the Caloris impact crater (orange). Messenger successfully entered orbit around Mercury in March 2011 and began sending back valuable data a month later.

darker hue. This turned out to be a massive hurricane that was scouring the face of the planet with winds of up to 2,500km/h.

By 2015 the American probe New Horizons, launched in January 2006, will have reached Pluto, the small frozen planet on the outer fringes of our Solar System and the last post before the intersidereal void. Pluto was only discovered in 1930, when it was originally classified as a planet, but in 2006 it was downgraded to a so-called 'dwarf' planet, as scientists now believe that it actually forms part of the Kuiper asteroid belt.

When the small US probe sends back the first images of Pluto, this will mean that all nine historical planets of our Solar System will have been visited, from Mercury, the closest to the Sun, to Pluto, the furthest away. Within the space of barely 60 years, humankind will have lifted the veil on its planetary neighbours. It is unlikely that manned planetary missions will be a reality in the very near future, given the huge costs involved, but the dream is still alive. In April 2010 President Barack Obama pledged that a man would set foot on a distant planet by 2025.

Internet telephony 1996

The growth of the Internet has given rise to a completely new form of telephone communication. Data is sent via either IP (Internet Protocol) or VoIP (Voice over Internet Protocol), in which the transmission of the human voice is no longer reliant on circuit switching, but rather on the digital networking communications method called 'packet switching'. This mode of data transfer was made possible by advances in electronics and information technology. Digitised and compressed, the voice is transmitted in the form of blocks of data (datagrams or 'packets') in the same way as bundles of data are sent across an ADSL connection. Internet telephony works through a combination of software accessing the IP communications protocol and various forms of network interface hardware used either by individuals or companies.

Free telephone access

In 1996 NetMeeting, which came bundled up with Microsoft's web browser, was one of the first applications to transmit the human voice via IP. Yet computers and dial-up modems (ADSL broadband was not then widespread) were not yet fast enough for it to really take off. In 2003 Skype software finally brought VoIP into its own. A headpiece connected to or integrated into the computer and Internet access enables users to talk for free with friends and family all around the world.

The technology continued to develop, with Internet Wi-Fi phones independent of computers. The cost of broadband connections also fell, with Internet service providers now offering IP telephony as part of their subscription package.

Alternative telecommunication
Using an Internet connection, with or without a Webcam, to make telephone calls is growing steadily in popularity. There is no longer even any need to sit in front of the computer at home; the latest Internet telephony applications are accessible to anyone on the move who is equipped with a smartphone and has access to an Internet Wi-Fi zone.

COFFEE-TIME INSPIRATION

In 1991 scientists in Cambridge developed the first Webcam to find out remotely whether a coffee machine in a commonroom at their lab was full, and so save themselves a wasted trip. Initially on a local network, the camera was hooked up to the Internet in 1993 and became a popular landmark of the early Web. Today, webcams are incorporated into screens on desktop and laptop PCs. They can be used to put Internet users in face-to-face contact or to provide surveillance of an area. But because images and voice are transmitted at the same time, the results can sometimes be jerky.

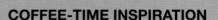

DIGITAL HD TELEVISION – 1996

Analogue TV bows out

While 'digital' and 'high definition' are now inextricably linked where TV is concerned, these two technologies actually developed in parallel for 20 years before converging. At the turn of the 21st century, this dual-track evolution has completely transformed television, bringing about the demise of analogue equipment and introducing massively larger screens than were ever previously available.

The first digital high-definition television programmes ever to be broadcast were transmitted in America in the summer of 1996 by stations affiliated to the CBS and NBC networks. But the history of high-definition TV goes back to Japan in the 1970s

Japan sets the pace

The Japanese state broadcaster Nippon Hoso Kyokai (NHK) developed the first high-definition analogue television system in conjunction with Panasonic. Called MUSE, this system boasted 1125 scanning lines, almost double the standard 625 lines at the time. By 1989 the MUSE system was widespread in Japan; homes there were equipped with satellite dishes, by far the most efficient way of receiving the impressive data stream entailed in the transmission of HDTV images. Around 10,000 decoders were sold, and a wide range of programmes were made in the format.

In 1981 a prototype of the MUSE system was demonstrated in Los Angeles. President Ronald Reagan announced that it would be in the country's interest to set up a nationwide HD television broadcast network across the United States. In March 1985 a US government working party known as the Advanced Television Systems Committee opted in favour of the Japanese system. Japan and the USA thus became the first countries to transmit analogue HDTV programmes.

Around this time, Europe was developing its own HD standard. The D2-MAC system, introduced in 1985, was a hybrid of analogue images and digital sound. But barely a year later, in the forum of the International Radio Consultative Committee, NHK and CBS tried to get the MUSE system adopted as the universal analogue standard. The Europeans contended that MUSE was incompatible with most existing broadcast equipment and moreover took up double the bandwidth of standard analogue TV. They also developed their own rival system, HD-MAC, a high-definition version of D2-MAC. But because they were unsure how durable any of these systems would be in practice, broadcasters dragged their feet over adopting HD, and the HD-MAC format was abandoned in 1993.

The advent of digital

New moves were already afoot to rejuvenate the idea of high-definition television. In 1990 the General Instrument Corporation (GI) of New York, which manufactured television equipment for professional use, put forward a proposal for a new, entirely digital, high-definition TV system. The technology would be capable of transmitting larger, crisper images than analogue, while being far more compact. In addition, the digital signal would be less susceptible to breaking up over long distances or when confronted with obstacles.

Big-screen entertainment
This huge LCD television screen measures 2.74m on the diagonal (the standard way of expressing screen size) and has a viewing angle of 176°. It was made by the Japanese electronics company Sharp in 2007.

DIGITAL HD TELEVISION – 1996

Analogue TV bows out

While 'digital' and 'high definition' are now inextricably linked where TV is concerned, these two technologies actually developed in parallel for 20 years before converging. At the turn of the 21st century, this dual-track evolution has completely transformed television, bringing about the demise of analogue equipment and introducing massively larger screens than were ever previously available.

The first digital high-definition television programmes ever to be broadcast were transmitted in America in the summer of 1996 by stations affiliated to the CBS and NBC networks. But the history of high-definition TV goes back to Japan in the 1970s

Japan sets the pace

The Japanese state broadcaster Nippon Hoso Kyokai (NHK) developed the first high-definition analogue television system in conjunction with Panasonic. Called MUSE, this system boasted 1125 scanning lines, almost double the standard 625 lines at the time. By 1989 the MUSE system was widespread in Japan; homes there were equipped with satellite dishes, by far the most efficient way of receiving the impressive data stream entailed in the transmission of HDTV images. Around 10,000 decoders were sold, and a wide range of programmes were made in the format.

In 1981 a prototype of the MUSE system was demonstrated in Los Angeles. President Ronald Reagan announced that it would be in the country's interest to set up a nationwide HD television broadcast network across the United States. In March 1985 a US government working party known as the Advanced Television Systems Committee opted in favour of the Japanese system. Japan and the USA thus became the first countries to transmit analogue HDTV programmes.

Around this time, Europe was developing its own HD standard. The D2-MAC system, introduced in 1985, was a hybrid of analogue images and digital sound. But barely a year later, in the forum of the International Radio Consultative Committee, NHK and CBS tried to get the MUSE system adopted as the universal analogue standard. The Europeans contended that MUSE was incompatible with

most existing broadcast equipment and moreover took up double the bandwidth of standard analogue TV. They also developed their own rival system, HD-MAC, a high-definition version of D2-MAC. But because they were unsure how durable any of these systems would be in practice, broadcasters dragged their feet over adopting HD, and the HD-MAC format was abandoned in 1993.

The advent of digital

New moves were already afoot to rejuvenate the idea of high-definition television. In 1990 the General Instrument Corporation (GI) of New York, which manufactured television equipment for professional use, put forward a proposal for a new, entirely digital, high-definition TV system. The technology would be capable of transmitting larger, crisper images than analogue, while being far more compact. In addition, the digital signal would be less susceptible to breaking up over long distances or when confronted with obstacles.

Big-screen entertainment
This huge LCD television screen measures 2.74m on the diagonal (the standard way of expressing screen size) and has a viewing angle of 176°. It was made by the Japanese electronics company Sharp in 2007.

providers began offering 'triple play' packages comprising telephone, Internet use and digital television access.

Gradual takeover

With the roll-out of digital terrestrial television (DTT) in Europe at the end of the 1990s, the digital revolution finally reached the traditional airwaves. Compatible with existing technology, it is transmitted by a network of terrestrial towers, just like its analogue forerunner, and is picked up by roof aerials in the same way. To receive digital TV, a user must install an external decoder in the form of a 'set-top' box on their analogue TV, or purchase a new digital-ready TV set. From 1998 on, DTT began in the UK, followed by

Variety at your fingertips
Digital television offers viewers an ever-wider choice of programmes and services, including 'On-Demand TV', a kind of virtual video store.

Within just a few years, HD spread like wildfire on US cable and satellite networks.

In Europe, meanwhile, a consortium of broadcasters, manufacturers and regulating authorities set about developing a digital broadcasting standard: DVB (Digital Video Broadcasting). The first experiments in digital transmission took place from 1996 onwards, with the launch of the specially dedicated satellite SES Astra 1. Before long, digital TV made it onto the Internet. Technical advances such as ADSL 2+ enabled larger and faster downloads via broadband, and Internet service

MULTIPLEXING

Hand-in-hand with digital television came the technique of multiplexing – the simultaneous transmission of multiple digital data streams ('packets') in one signal over a shared bandwidth. A demultiplexer in the television tuner sorts out these packets in order to screen the programme in its entirety. Multiplexing means that the cost of occupying a particular bandwidth can be split between different users. This has seen the emergence of many new, low-budget channels.

Unwanted innovation
Mobile personal televisions have never really caught on. In a 2009 survey, around two-thirds of people questioned expressed little or no interest in this technology.

MOBILE TV

Television access from mobile phones, aka digital multimedia broadcasting (DMB), was pioneered in Japan in 2003. Within two years it had spread to India and notably South Korea, where it became hugely popular. Other countries followed, but DMB has failed to take off in the UK, Germany and elsewhere.

Sweden and Spain, and then most of the rest of Europe. Its beginnings were tentative, with expensive set-top boxes, few channels, patchy coverage, and transmissions only in standard definition. Yet more and more networks are investing in HD production facilities. The European Union recommended that most countries switch over by 2012, but Luxembourg and the Netherlands completed the transition to DTT as early as 2006. The analogue signal will presently be phased out across Europe, and then the United States.

The driving force behind the adoption of digital television has not only been the wide choice of channels, but also the advent of Video on Demand (VOD), which allows viewers to rent films directly through their television. Refinements like Time Shifting also allow people to record programmes and store them temporarily on an internal hard-drive for later viewing. The modern TV is far slimmer than its old cathode-ray precursor, but has expanded hugely in terms of screen size. High-definition digital television truly has transformed the flickering 'box' in the corner of the room into a home cinema.

CLEAR CHOICE

In 2008 the welter of confusing specifications for high-definition TVs was simplified into two standard designations: HDTV, denoting a screen fitted with a tuner that displays 720 pixels of vertical resolution; and HDTV 1080p, sometimes called 'Full HD', with 1080 pixels.

VIDEO COMPRESSION

Digitisation of a video involves replacing the variations in electrical amplitude in which the video-audio signal is encoded by a sequence of binary data (0s and 1s). Yet data digitised in this way takes up ten times the space. Plus, a high-definition video is six times larger again than one in standard definition. To overcome this problem, MPEG compression formats only send the code for those parts of an image that have changed by comparison with the previous image. This is the reason why channels broadcasting programmes where the image is constantly changing, such as sports or action films, use more bandwidth than, say, a channel devoted to political debates.

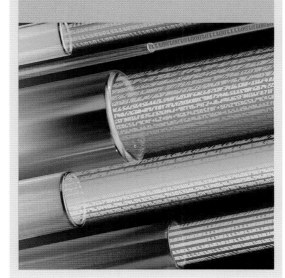

The perfect picture
Two researchers at Sandia National Laboratory in New Mexico, USA, study an image on a high-definition computer screen (above). With a resolution of 20 million pixels, the screen was designed to enable scientists to visualise large amounts of data. To create the ultra HD image, the system uses 64 computers in parallel and 16 projectors.

Fast transmission
Fibre-optic cables like these (left) enable data to be transferred at speeds of 100 megabits (Mb) per second, without any loss of quality in the signal (as compared to 30Mb per second via ADSL using copper telephone cables).

Plasma screen TVs 1997

Brand-new TV
When it was launched in 2002, Samsung's top-of-the-range plasma screen (right), measuring 1.6m on the diagonal but just 9cm deep, was one of the largest and slimmest televisions on the market.

Plasma screen technology is based on the principle of ionised gases emitting light. Trapped within millions of tiny capsules, this gas, a mixture of argon and xenon, changes its state when an electrical impulse is passed through it and becomes plasma. This substance sends out ultraviolet radiation, which in turn activates a layer of phosphorus coating the capsules. Depending upon the intensity and number of electrical charges, the capsules effectively become cells that light up and reproduce 256 gradations of colour from a basic palette of red, blue and green. Each cell represents one pixel, which combine to make

New TV generation
Panasonic plasma televisions (above) on display in 2008 at the IFA fair in Berlin, the world's largest trade show for consumer electronics.

up the entire image displayed. The plasma cell layer is sandwiched between two sheets of glass, which form the television's flat screen.

The plasma screen was invented in 1964 by two professors at the University of Illinois, Donald L Bitzer and H Gene Slottow. Their prototype comprised a small matrix of 4 x 4 pixels. The device could only output text in monochrome, either orange or green, thanks to the use of neon, which was later replaced. By 1967 the size of the screens had increased fourfold, but they were still far from being anything more than 'proof-of-concept' testbeds. In this early stage, this expensive

technology failed to excite any commercial interest among electronics manufacturers. A simpler and less costly TV technology – the cathode-ray tube, invented in 1907 and in use since 1933 – had long cornered the market.

Unrivalled picture quality

In 1992 the plasma screen concept was revived by the Japanese firm Fujitsu, which built on Bitzer and Slottow's research to produce the first colour plasma display. Three years later Sony, in partnership with the firm Tektronik, developed its 'plasmatron' system (PALC), a hybrid of liquid crystal display (LCD) and plasma technology. The first plasma screen television, manufactured by Pioneer, went on sale in 1997. The public was captivated by its clarity of image, far superior to anything a cathode-ray tube could produce – and better even than LCD. And the size of these early plasma screens was amazing, upward of 1.5m diagonally, offering big-screen entertainment in people's homes.

Plasma versus LCD

Unlike LCD screens, plasma screens actually produce light. Their great selling points are: the luminosity and high contrast of the image; their large format; their extreme flatness; the depth of black they display; and their wide viewing angle. On the downside they remain expensive, they consume a lot of electricity and they have a relatively short life. From the early 2000s onwards, they have been challenged in the home entertainment market by LCD screens, which were formerly used only for computer displays. While plasma continues to dominate for big-screen home cinemas, it accounts for just 7 per cent of the total television market, with LCD having captured all the rest (cathode-ray TVs are no longer made). And the tide is running in favour of LCD. Making LCD televisions is very similar to the manufacture of semi-conductors, a realm in which many electronics companies are already well-versed. Another contender is the organic light-emitting diode (OLED), an up-and-coming big-screen technology.

Flexible screens

The first flexible TV screens appeared in 2010. Still at the prototype stage, these revolutionary new screens exploit OLED technology. This process, pioneered by Kodak, enables any screen, however slim, to emit light when an electric current is passed through it. Their ultra-thinness comes from the fact that they do not need the backlighting required by LCD equipment. Researchers from the Japanese audiovisual group NHK are at the forefront of the technology; in 2009 they introduced a 14cm flexible screen. The American Universal Display Corporation, Epson and Samsung have also launched flexible screens.

Light sandwich
Plasma screen technology visualised in a computer-generated cutaway image (below). Many tiny cells sandwiched between two panels of glass contain a mixture of noble gases which turns to plasma when electrically charged, in turn exciting a phosphorus layer to emit light.

CUTTING-EDGE ASIA

Japan, South Korea and Taiwan are in the vanguard of flatscreen TV technology. Companies such as Panasonic, Samsung and LG Electronics are the world's leading producers of plasma screens. Manufacture of LCD screens is also heavily concentrated in the region. Following the historic lead taken by companies in these Asian countries in miniaturising electronic components, it was a natural step for them to become involved in the television and computer display markets. Their unmatched expertise in this field comes from long years of research and development work, and also from production facilities that are at the cutting edge of high-tech.

Roll-up viewing
Japanese electronics companies have pioneered flexible display screens that can be unrolled like a poster for viewing high-definition television or movies, then rolled up again for easy storage.

Making motors eco-friendly

In 1997 the Japanese car-maker Toyota unveiled the world's first volume hybrid car, the Prius. Using a combination of an internal combustion engine and an electric motor, hybrid cars were hailed as a viable alternative to purely electric vehicles.

Although electrically powered cars were developed in the early days of motoring, the internal combustion engine offered drivers better performance and it soon won out over the alternative competition. But at the start of the 21st century, with petrol becoming a scarcer and increasingly expensive commodity, and the need to limit greenhouse-gas emissions becoming a priority, the electric motor began to make a comeback. Even so, its chief shortcoming still remains: the batteries are too bulky and take too long to charge. There is also a question mark over longevity and electric motors still do not allow drivers the same freedom as a tankful of petrol or diesel.

Early hybrid experiments

It has taken a century of development for hybrid cars to come on the market in a major way, but the concept has been around since the infancy of the automobile. At the 1900 Universal Exposition in Paris, the Austrian engineer Ferdinand Porsche, who was employed by the automobile manufacturer Jacob Lohner, won a gold medal for his petrol-electric 'Semper Vivus' car. Porsche's design involved a small internal combustion engine activating a generator, which supplied two electric motors mounted in the wheel hubs. Other car manufacturers followed suit with their own hybrids: Krieger (1903) and Mildé & Cie (1904) in France, Auto-Mixte (1906) in Belgium, and the Woods Motor Vehicle Company in Chicago which produced hybrid gas-electric models. Yet one after the other, all these hybrid cars disappeared and were forgotten.

In an attempt to improve performance from their petrol engines, some vehicle manufacturers continued on the hybrid path until 1910. Yet by then the internal combustion engine had made such rapid advances that it easily outstripped anything that the hybrid vehicles could offer. The development of mixed-fuel automobiles was effectively mothballed for more than half a century, only periodically being resuscitated when fuel was short due to rationing in wartime.

Nothing new
Electric cars, like this Baker Model V 'Electric Victoria' of 1910, have been around since the early days of motoring. The American Baker Motor Vehicle Company was a pioneer of this form of propulsion, which offered clean, quiet and reliable transportation.

Proto-hybrid power
A racing version of the Lohner–Porsche 'Semper Vivus' car launched in 1910 at the Geneva Motor Show (above). It combined a 480-horsepower petrol engine with two hub-mounted electric motors, each with a capacity of 82hp.

FULL HYBRIDS

In so-called 'full hybrid' vehicles, like the Toyota Prius, the electric and internal combustion engines are designed to alternate automatically, as appropriate. So at low speeds around town, the electric motor takes over, powering the car over a maximum range of 5km. The electric motor acts like a dynamo, storing the kinetic energy of the car during braking and recycling this energy into more power. On the open road, or whenever the battery is low, the petrol engine takes up the baton, providing a surplus of energy that recharges the battery. The electric motor also provides a boost whenever a short surge of power is called for, such as when accelerating to overtake, or climbing a steep hill.

Reviving the hybrid

It was only in the 1970s, after the shock of the first oil crisis, that car-makers began to take a serious interest in hybrid vehicles once more. In 1973 the German manufacturer Volkswagen produced a hybrid petrol-electric car. Three years later a sports car using a revolutionary new combination of electric and gas-turbine engines rolled off the production line of the Japanese manufacturer Toyota. Audi entered the fray in 1989.

Whereas manufacture of hybrid cars was at first confined to limited production runs, things really got going in 1997 when Toyota took the bold step of beginning volume production of their Prius model, destined originally for the Japanese home market. This multipurpose vehicle had a large, comfortable passenger compartment and combined the advantages of a family cruiser suitable for long-distance runs with the fuel-efficiency of a small urban runabout. Toyota sold more than 18,000 of their first-generation Prius.

In 1999 Honda, the other Japanese automobile giant, pitched for the US market with its Insight model. Toyota responded with a four-door saloon version of the Prius. With fully electric cars confined to about-town use and alternative clean-engine technology, such as fuel cells or compressed air, still very much at the R&D stage, other car manufacturers soon joined the hybrid

bandwagon: Audi (in 1997), Ford (2004), General Motors (2006), Lexus, Nissan (2007) and finally Chevrolet, Cadillac, Hyundai and Mercedes-Benz in 2009. By the end of 2009 there were reckoned to be around 2.5 million hybrids on the road throughout the world, mainly concentrated in Japan, the United States and Europe. At present, the market leaders in the field are Toyota, Honda and Ford.

Keeping check on energy use
The energy monitor on a 2004 Toyota Prius (below). The dashboard panel shows drivers which power source the car is using at any one time. The electric battery recharges itself when the car slows down or brakes.

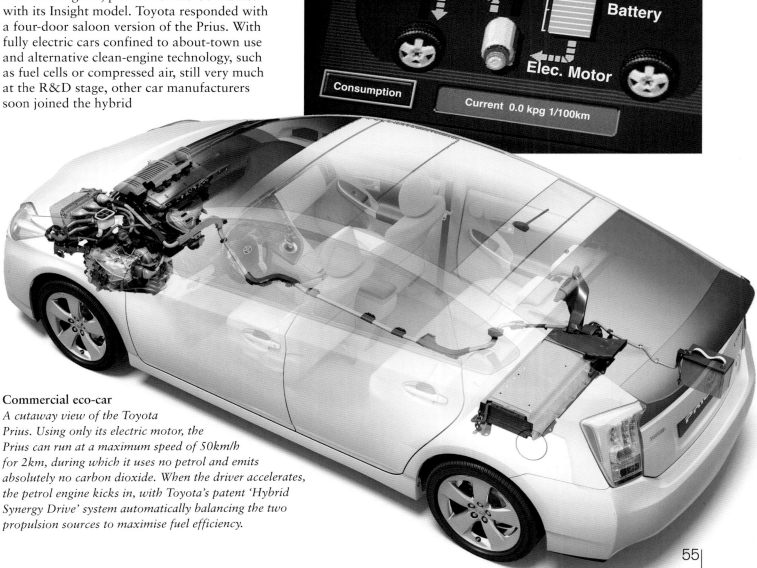

Commercial eco-car
A cutaway view of the Toyota Prius. Using only its electric motor, the Prius can run at a maximum speed of 50km/h for 2km, during which it uses no petrol and emits absolutely no carbon dioxide. When the driver accelerates, the petrol engine kicks in, with Toyota's patent 'Hybrid Synergy Drive' system automatically balancing the two propulsion sources to maximise fuel efficiency.

Downloading digital music

In 1979, the same year that Sony launched the Walkman, which became a huge international success, a British inventor named Kane Kramer dreamt up a revolutionary portable personal music player the size of a credit card. His device was equipped with an LCD screen, 4-way navigation buttons, and a memory of 8 megabytes, enough for just over three minutes of playing time. This was the ancestor of MP3 players, which eventually appeared on the scene in 1998.

Three generations of sound
A vinyl LP, CD and MP3 player (above). Less than 60 years separate the first vinyl records introduced in the 1940s) from MP3 players.

Kane Kramer envisaged that his device, which he called the IXI, would tap into a music download service operating over telephone lines. He filed patents for the IXI between 1985 and 1987 but, unable to raise the start-up capital for development, he let the patents lapse and his designs came into the public domain. Apple subsequently picked up the idea and developed it over a period of 13 years.

Meanwhile, the cassette/radio Sony Walkman enjoyed unrivalled success up until 1982, when Philips and Sony jointly launched the Compact Disc. The first portable CD player came on the market two years later. But the drawback of all these portable music players was that the user needed to carry around a stack of cassettes or CDs.

To overcome this problem, in 1992 Sony introduced the MiniDisc, which was smaller than a CD but held the same amount of music thanks to a specially devised audio compression system. The format was a hit in Japan, but not in the West, where MiniDiscs remained expensive with only a limited catalogue of artists available.

The rise of the MP3

In the 1990s, one result to emerge from the EUREKA project – a working group set up to develop new technologies within the European Union – was a new audio compression format known as the MPEG-1/2 Audio Layer 3, better known by its abbreviation MP3. The

MP3 COMPRESSION

Audio compression in the MP3 format consists of suppressing sounds that the human ear cannot hear and eliminating those that are drowned out by other louder sounds. The compression algorithm also economises on space by limiting the encoding of repetitive sections of music. The rate of compression can be raised or lowered according to whether one wants to prioritise sound quality or minimise file size. Various other formats exist alongside MP3, including OGG Vorbis, Windows Media Audio (WMA), ATRAC, AAC, and FLAC.

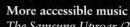

More accessible music
The Samsung Uproar (2000), the first cellphobe with MP3 capability, had an Internet browser enabling users to access music download sites directly. This dispensed with the need for a fixed computer terminal and CDs to store the downloaded clips on.

FLASH MEMORY

Flash memory is a rewritable storage facility for digital information. It is 'non-volatile', which means it maintains the data even without any power input. Unlike a hard disk, it has no moving parts and is therefore far more durable.

format enabled audio files to be compressed to one-twelfth of their original size, with minimal loss of sound quality. The first device that could read MP3 files was the 'Listen Up Player' made by the US firm Audio Highway, which could download an hour of music onto its flash memory from a dedicated website. It went on sale in 1997, but was too expensive to compete with the older generation of portable players.

Europe's first MP3 player, the MPMan F10, appeared in 1998. Its 32Mb of flash memory could hold half an hour of music. The device was soon overshadowed by the higher-performance Rio PMP300 from the Californian manufacturer Diamond Multimedia. But it was the American computer giant Apple that brought Kramer's concept to full fruition, with the launch of the iPod in October 2001. As with many Apple products, its clean design and ease of use wowed the public. The first iPods had a 1.8-inch hard drive holding 5Gb of data, or 83 hours of music; the capacity doubled the following year. A design classic, the iPod was soon the world's most popular digital player.

USB mini-players

As the cost of flash memory came down, USB sticks equipped with a headphone jack and navigation buttons came on the market in 2002, ushering in a whole new range of ultra-compact music players. The compressed sound was undoubtedly inferior to that on a CD, but good enough for listening to in noisy surroundings. Around the same time, mobile phone manufacturers began adding more functions to their devices: the first cellphone with an MP3 play facility was the Samsung Uproar, launched in South Korea in 2000. This marked the beginning of a rapidly expanding new market: by 2005, sales of mobiles capable of reading music files outstripped those of pure MP3 players for the first time. Since then, smartphones have come to dominate the market for music on the move.

Mobile music mania
By 2007 it was estimated that some 4 million adults in the UK were using their mobile phones as MP3 players. As with most technological innovations, this trend is most prevalent among young people.

DIGITAL RIGHTS

In order to avoid any accusation that they were promoting piracy, several legal music download sites tried incorporating digital rights management (DRM) software within the files they provided. This limited their use in terms, say, of the number of times they could be played, the number of platforms they could be copied onto, or their expiry date, but the measures rendered the files unreadable on certain players. The public voted with their feet and rejected this 'rental' style of selling. Accordingly, EMI dropped DRM as unworkable in 2007, followed by other major copyright holders.

Targeted advertising
Eye-catching TV and poster campaigns, seen here in San Francisco in 2007, helped Apple's iPod to conquer the market in portable media players. Apple also introduced its own iTunes software for users to purchase and manage their music files.

Compact style
The iPod Nano, launched in 2005, has already been through five generations. This tiny device weighs less than 40 grams and can deliver 24 hours of non-stop music.

The controversy over music downloading

From 1997 onwards, a number of legal Internet sites began offering downloads of music files, either for free or as a paying service. But the Napster music store, a peer-to-peer free file sharing service launched in 1999, became a victim of its own success. In barely two years, it attracted more than 60 million users, but the record companies were losing out on their royalties. They counterattacked through the courts, forcing Napster to withdraw its service in 2001 on the grounds that it had infringed the intellectual property rights of artists.

Even so, the filesharing genie was now out of the bottle and other sites sprang up to take its place. Between 1999 and 2003, CD sales fell 23 per cent by volume and by 16 per cent by revenue. The record labels blamed piracy and lobbied for legislation; the debate is still ongoing. In the meantime, they reached an accord with legitimate file-sharing operations. In April 2000, for example, Sony Music Entertainment in partnership with the Universal Music Group introduced their own online music site. Sales of music clips through file-sharing sites and the downloading of tunes for ringtones on mobile phones now represent a growing source of income for artists. By 2006 CD sales had fallen to 55 per cent of music revenue worldwide.

A DANGER TO HEARING?

The headphones on iPods and MP3 players transmit sounds at a maximum amplitude of between 80 and 120 decibels of sound pressure level (dBSPL). Though studies indicate that beyond 87 decibels the risk of harm to one's hearing increases with length of exposure, unequivocal damage during just a few minutes of listening occurs only when levels are in excess of 110 decibels. Research suggests there is a significant incidence of hearing loss in music-player users aged between 15 and 19. Some jurisdictions now prevent manufacturers from supplying equipment that can exceed 100 dBSPL. Experts are agreed that the current generation runs the risk of incurring serious hearing loss by the age of 50 to 55, some ten years earlier than preceding generations.

PODCASTS

With the rise of Apple's portable digital player, radio and TV stations caught on to the idea of distributing their programmes as podcasts. These digital media files – the word 'podcast' is a portmanteau of 'iPod' and 'broadcast' – enable people to download items they have missed 'live' in order to listen to them at a time of their choosing.

Viagra® 1998

Pep pills

The blue lozenges of Viagra®, made by Pfizer, dominate over rival products such as Levitra®, made by Bayer, and Cialis®, made by Eli Lilly.

Marketed under the brand name Viagra®, sildenafil citrate acts by suppressing an enzyme that restricts the passage of blood into the penis. During sexual stimulation, it can thus help to overcome erectile dysfunction by increasing the blood flow. The drug was synthesised by a team of pharmacists working at the Pfizer Laboratories at Sandwich in Kent, led by Peter Dunn and Albert Wood. Originally developed as a way of treating arterial hypertension and angina, the results of the first clinical trials led Pfizer to promote its benefits in countering erectile impotence brought on by conditions such as diabetes, high blood pressure or raised cholesterol. Viagra® was patented in 1996 and approved by the US Federal Drugs Administration on 27 March, 1998. The success of the blue lozenge-shaped pills was instant. By 2000 Viagra® sales accounted for 92 per cent of the global market in prescription drugs for erectile problems, valued at around a billion dollars. The patent for Viagra® is due to lapse in 2011, enabling the sale of cheaper generic alternatives. This should put an end to the rogue Internet trade in counterfeit anti-impotence drugs.

Energy-saving lightbulbs 1998

Compact fluorescent lightbulbs (CFLs), also called low-energy or energy-saving bulbs, were the brainchild of French inventors Henri Courier de Méré and Boune Hieng Phone Tiang. They have many advantages over the traditional incandescent lightbulb, notably a lifespan 6 to 15 times longer and enhanced performance of 60 to 70 lumens per Watt, as against 14–25lm/W, which adds up to huge savings in electricity usage. A 15W CFL has the light intensity of a 60W incandescent bulb, achieved by using an electronic device to boost the sinusoidal frequency of the current from 50 to 30,000Hz. It has been estimated that 10 billion CFLs installed worldwide would cut CO_2 emissions by 1 per cent. Because of this, incandescent bulbs are set to be phased out in Europe by 2012, and countries around the world have similar ambitions. Yet CFLs do have drawbacks: they are more expensive and bulkier than incandescents; they take several minutes to reach full power; they contain mercury (see box below); and they produce a colder light. In areas where electricity comes from hydro or nuclear power, switching to CFLs would lose the heat given off by traditional bulbs and actually increase greenhouse gases from natural gas burned for central heating.

Longlife light

Replacing all incandescent lightbulbs with low-energy bulbs like this one (right) is projected to save 8 terawatt-hours of electricity consumption by 2016. This equates to twice the annual electricity usage of a city of several million inhabitants.

NOT SO 'ECO-FRIENDLY'

One drawback of the energy-saving lightbulb is that once its working life is at an end, it becomes toxic waste. This is because the fluorescent tube contains a harmful mercury-vapour gas. A special process is required to dispose of them safely. If they break in situ, the room should be cleared and thoroughly aired. Mercury has also caused health problems for workers making CFLs.

Ever faster and ever more distant

In 1998 two teams of astronomers at the University of Berkeley in California were astonished to discover that the universe is expanding at an ever-increasing rate. Although Edwin Hubble had presented convincing evidence in the late 1920s to show that the universe was expanding, the acceleration of that expansion was completely unforeseen.

Cosmological redshift
The accelerating expansion of the universe manifests itself in light, coming to us from a distant object in space, shifting to the red end of the spectrum. Light sources in deep space (above right) display redshift corresponding to the rate of increase of their distance from Earth.

More than a decade after the discovery at Berkeley, astronmers are still trying to explain what is causing the universe to expand at an ever-faster rate. In the ousted classic theory of a universe that is expanding but ever-more slowly, the explanation was straightforward enough: some 13.7 billion years ago, the universe originated from a single, infinitely dense point (a 'singularity'), from which it then began to expand, as after an explosion. When Einstein revised his general theory of relativity in the light of Hubble's discovery (taking out of his equations the 'cosmological constant' he had wrongly introduced to try to corroborate a static universe), he reached the

conclusion that the quantity (or density) of matter in the universe generates a global gravitational effect that gradually slows expansion. This seemed to settle the matter.

Blast from the past

Research by the Berkeley astronomers Adam Riess and Saul Perlmutter indicated that the slowing of the expansion of the universe pertained at most to just the first 10 billion

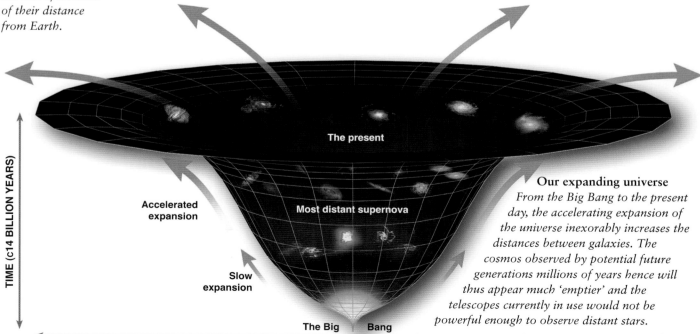

Our expanding universe
From the Big Bang to the present day, the accelerating expansion of the universe inexorably increases the distances between galaxies. The cosmos observed by potential future generations millions of years hence will thus appear much 'emptier' and the telescopes currently in use would not be powerful enough to observe distant stars.

TIME (c14 BILLION YEARS)

The present

Accelerated expansion

Most distant supernova

Slow expansion

The Big Bang

EXPANSION OF THE UNIVERSE

years after the Big Bang. In other words, for the most recent 4–5 billion years of the existence of the universe, it has been expanding at an accelerating rate. This inevitably raised the question of what was responsible for this. Einstein's equations on relativity had nothing to contribute, except for one small detail: the discarded concept of the 'cosmological constant'. This hypothetical term, which Einstein added in the margin of his calculations in order to mathematically counterbalance the effect of expansion, had fallen into disrepute after observation of the Hubble redshift. Einstein himself famously described it as the 'biggest blunder' of his career.

Dark energy

In 1998 the cosmological constant was rehabilitated, since it was the only factor that could square the equations with the observed fact of an accelerating expansion – and thereby save the whole theoretical basis of cosmology. Einstein had imputed to it a positive value, counteracting the supposedly contracting effect of gravity on what he assumed was a universe at equilibrium. By factoring it back into what was now known to be a dynamic universe as a *negative* value, scientists were able to account for cosmic expansion.

It was then a question of determining what physical force this constant represented. It appeared that there was a form of pressure, or 'repellent energy', bearing down on space which counteracted the attractive force of gravity. This new hypothetical form of energy was dubbed 'dark energy' (not to be confused with that other great enigma of astrophysics, dark matter). In the current standard model of cosmology, dark energy accounts for 73 per cent of total mass-energy of the universe.

SUPERNOVAE AND EXPANSION

To observe the accelerating expansion of the universe, Adam Riess and Paul Perlmutter studied several Type 1a supernovae in different distant galaxies. The key factor about this class of supernova is that they all have the same brightness. Thus, according to their degree of apparent luminosity as seen from Earth, the scientists could work out their distance and speed. It emerged that the more distant they are, the greater the speed at which they are receding from us. This provided the conclusive proof of cosmic acceleration.

TOWARDS A 'BIG RIP'?

Various scenarios have been painted for the ultimate fate of the universe. One relatively optimistic view is that in tens of billions of years' time, all the galaxy clusters will be so far removed from one another that they will be unable to interact. In contrast, a pessimistic hypothesis known as the 'Big Rip' theory predicts that the pressure of expansion will increase to the point where all matter in the universe is torn apart; not only galaxies will separate, but also the stars and planets, even molecules and atoms. All that will remain will be a gas of extremely diffuse particles.

The challenge of the 21st century

One major strand of recent research has been to try to substantiate dark energy. Some observations by the WMAP satellite and ground-based telescopes seem indirectly to indicate its presence. But proving its existence and devising a theory to explain its physical nature remain key challenges for 21st-century astrophysicists.

Measuring the universe
A supernova is the explosive death of a star. Supernova SN1994D in the galaxy NGC 4526, part of the Virgo cluster of galaxies – visible below as the bright point at bottom left – was a Type 1a supernova, all of which have the same brightness. One of the tasks of the American WMAP satellite (below left) is to observe such supernovae and use them to calculate distances within our universe.

Digital media access

Data is transmitted to ADSL subscribers by various routes. The modem is the hub through which a variety of digital services arrive in the home; plugged into a phone socket, it distributes information to the television, computer and phone. Upstream from the phone socket, a multiplexer (DSLAM) at the phone company's exchange provides a high-speed connection between different servers providing television, Internet and multimedia content.

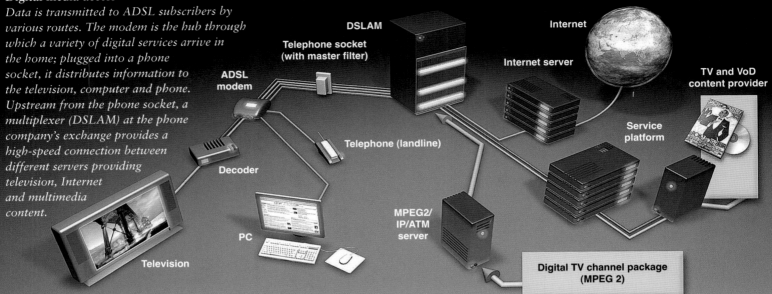

ADSL 1998

Digital divide
In 2009, according to a report by the European Commission, 93 per cent of Europeans had access to high-speed broadband services, but in rural areas this figure could fall as low as 50 per cent. Below: a public Net access facility at a conference in France.

Modern telephone networks allow people to do much more than simply call one another. They can also be used to transmit data via fax or across the Internet through a modem. In 1996, while people were still using slow dial-up modems to send information downline across the Net, the American BellCore Labs introduced the first Digital Subscriber Line (DSL) network. This technology used the existing telephone network to send much larger files than had previously been possible, with download speeds increasing from 56KB/sec to 2MB/sec. In the process, it produced a whole range of new communications technologies.

FAST BROADBAND

ADSL offers download speeds of between 1 and 28MB/sec. A key factor is the distance from the phone socket in the user's home to the local exchange, an infrastructure that the telephone company puts at the disposal of all ISPs. To get the fastest download speeds, the user must be within 2km of the exchange. This means that city dwellers are far better placed than those living in the countryside, and they also have access to cable networks, which can offer download speeds of up to 100 MB/sec.

Cornering the market

The most widespread and successful of these was ADSL – Asymmetric Digital Subscriber Line. It was promoted by a special UN agency, the International Telecommunication Union, and boosted by the failure of fibre optic networks to gain a major market share in the early 1990s. Telephone companies were also keen to counter the spread of cable networks, which were five times faster. They achieved this by exploiting ADSL's potential for wide geographical coverage. Another advantage was that ADSL used existing copper-wire telephone lines, so did not require installation of a separate cable or extra connection. All that was needed was a router to transfer data from the Internet Service Provider through the telephone socket. As ADSL usage grew, ISPs diversified the packages they sold to subscribers, offering a wide range of services.

WiFi networks 1999

Hands free
A Bluetooth wireless headset (right) allows hands-free operation of a mobile phone. Mostly used for voice transmission, the headset can also be used at close proximity to activate and transmit data to other Bluetooth-enabled devices in the home, such as a wireless mouse and keyboard, or gaming consoles.

Remote access
A laptop user logs on at a WiFi hotspot in the remote northwest Scottish Highlands. In the EU, Norway and Belgium lead the field in usage of WiFi networks.

The use of short-range radio waves for data transmission became a reality in 1999 with the introduction of 'WiFi' (Wireless Fidelity') technology. Also known as 802.11b, WiFi is based on a standard set by the Institute of Electrical and Electronic Engineers (IEEE), a global organisation. Pioneered by Apple under the trademark name of AirPort, the technology first came to public attention in June 2000, when a non-profit organisation in Seattle launched a locally-owned wireless community network: terminals were set up to mark the area covered and all users could get wireless broadband Internet access, as long as they had an adapter on their PC.

WiFi offers users several advantages: it makes the most of the mobility possible with laptops and other portable devices; it is easy and quick to install; and it is relatively low cost. Disadvantages include problems of security as near-neighbours can piggy-back on an unsecured WiFi network; periodic loss of signal; and an effective radius of around 30m at best – less if the signal encounters an obstacle such as a wall. Despite such drawbacks, WiFi provides fast broadband connection (6MB/sec) on 2.4GHz.

WiFi, WiMax and ZigBee

All modems soon came fitted with a WiFi function and most computers, including laptops and notebooks, had an adapter

installed as a matter of course. From 2002 on, WiFi access began to spread into the public domain, with terminals set up around a designated area so that anyone could connect to the Internet; sometimes, this service came free of charge. Alternative technologies also began to appear to rival WiFi: WiMax, for example, is an enhanced form of wireless network with a radius seven times greater than WiFi, but the adapters are expensive; 3G mobile phone networks also give users fast broadband connection. Finally, ZigBee wireless personal area networks, similar to Bluetooth, were launched from 2003 but failed to make a significant impact on the market.

> **BLUETOOTH**
> Another open wireless technology standard that first saw the light of day in 1999 is Bluetooth. Emulating the serial port found on all computers, Bluetooth technology allows PCs to connect wirelessly to a number of peripheral devices, such as the keyboard, mouse, printer, mobile phones and digital cameras, and enables them to communicate with one another. Its range is around 2–3m and it operates on a 2.4GHz waveband.

Wi-Fi
* hot spot
new ways of making you talk™

Healthy eating

In the late 1990s, the food industry developed a healthier new range of products. Apart from their general nutritional benefits, these enriched or modified foodstuffs targeted their effect on certain vital functions of the human body. This sector today is dominated by probiotics, foods containing Omega-3 and plant sterols.

The chiller cabinets in modern supermarkets are full of a bewildering array of products claiming to improve health, from margarines enriched with plant sterols and spreads high in Omega-3, to yogurts with so-called 'active bifidus' (bifidobacteria) and fruit juices laced with multivitamins. These have been developed to promote and exploit a growing trend towards health consciousness in daily diets.

A long history

The concept of healthfoods is far from new. In Ancient Greece, the physician Hippocrates (460–359 BC) counselled 'Let your food be your medicine and your medicine be your food'. Dietetics formed one of the pillars of traditional Chinese medicine and of the ancient Ayurvedic medicine of India. But as urbanisation and industrialisation took hold, the emphasis shifted first onto getting enough to eat and then onto convenience. In the increasing prosperity of the post-war world, ready access to plentiful, calorie-rich foods combined with an ever-more sedentary lifestyle increased the prevalence of obesity and eating disorders. It was in this context that the first products came on the market containing less sugar and fats than normal processed foods.

The first to arrive was the 'Taillefine' brand of dairy products, beginning in 1964 with a fromage frais containing zero fat. Aspartame, an artificial non-saccharide sweetener introduced in the United States in 1974, opened the way for the manufacture of soft drinks with non-fattening sweeteners. Coca-Cola jumped on the low-calorie bandwagon in 1982 when it launched Diet Coke as an alternative to its high-sugar flagship product.

The craze for healthfoods has expanded in the 1990s, and the health benefits of foods such as garlic (aids circulation and helps to

Apothecaries' favourite
Among medicinal plants, thyme (above) has been known since ancient times for anti-inflammatory, antiseptic and invigorating properties. Either drunk as an infusion or added to a hot bath, it was used to ward off common winter ailments like colds, flu and throat infections.

Traditional preparation
In the ancient Japanese tea ceremony, green tea known as matcha is beaten with a bamboo whisk (left). Two cups of this tea have the same antioxidant effect as seven glasses of orange juice or 20 glasses of apple juice.

new products in the 'functional food' category. To a great extent, marketing was at work here, blurring the boundaries between a wide range of different dietetic products, functional foods and food supplements. Before long, national food regulation agencies stepped in, requiring more precise labelling and outlawing any misleading advertising claims concerning the health-giving properties of foods.

Helping digestion

Foods containing probiotics (live micro-organisms that improve the microbial balance in the intestines) are some of the most popular products on the market. The benefits of fermented milk were revealed from the beginning of the 20th century onwards by

Added bacteria for health?
Bifidobacteria, shown here (above) in a magnified microscope image, added as probiotics to yogurts (left) and other foodstuffs have been the subject of some controversy. From 2010, the European Food Security Agency has required scientific proof of the health benefits of such additives before claims can be printed on packaging.

Warding off illness
The health benefits of this pungent allium bulb are believed to stem from its high sulphur content and its plentiful antioxidants, which counteract free radicals.

fight infections), honey and pineapple have become better understood. Marketing for grapefruit claimed it could 'burn off' fats. The food processing industry, meanwhile, was creating products enriched with vitamins and minerals. This led to 'functional foods', new foodstuffs midway between food and medicine.

The magic of marketing

The concept of functional foods came from Japan, where the acronym FOSHU (Foods for Specified Health Use) was coined in 1984. When these products were exported to the United States, the Americans came up with the term 'nutraceutic' for them (a compound of 'nutritious' and 'pharmaceutical'). They soon caught on in Europe as well. The designation 'functional foods' indicates that they have been devised to act on specific physiological functions, such as improving bowel function or reducing hypertension (high blood pressure).

By the mid-1990s the healthfood market was in full swing, with around 30 per cent of

KEEP YOUNG AND BEAUTIFUL

Folk wisdom once urged people to eat carrots for a better complexion. The modern buzzword for foods that supposedly improve your skin is 'dermonutrition'. Under this category come such unlikely products as Microfluid Technology's 'Sun Water', sold as an aid to tanning; marshmallows containing collagen (sold by the Eiwa company in Japan); and chocolate rich in antioxidants to improve skin tone (New Tree and Acticoa both produce such bars).

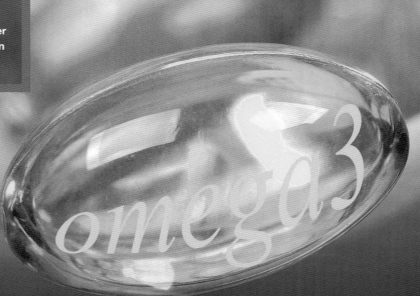

OMEGA-3: THE WONDER ACID

The benefits of fatty acids known as Omega-3 (or n-3) acids were first discovered among the Inuit people of Greenland, who ate large amounts of fat from oily fish and seafood but suffered almost no cardiovascular disease. In addition to reducing blood pressure and heart disease, they may have anti-cancer properties and even prevent the progression of certain psychotic disorders in children and adolescents.

Health capsule
Omega-3 capsules (above right) taken as a dietary supplement can effectively take the place of regular consumption of fish rich in these fatty acids. They are the modern equivalent of cod-liver oil, now also available as capsules, but once forced into children as a daily spoonful to promote growth and a healthy immune system.

the research of Élie Metchnikoff of the Pasteur Institute, who won the Nobel prize for medicine in 1908. The term 'probiotic' (literally, 'for life') was introduced in 1954. From 1984 on, various studies have shown that lactic bacteria in yogurts – *Streptococcus thermophilus* and *Lactobacillus bulgaricus* – encourage the digestion of lactose. The first dairy products containing bifidobacteria – intestinal microflora thought to prevent bowel disease – appeared in the 1980s. Other strains of probiotics followed: *Lactobacillus acidophilus* 1, added to Nestlé's Nesvita fruit yogurts from late 1994, and *Lactobacillus casei*, later relabelled *L. casei defensis* and used in Danone's Actimel range from 1997. These products owed their success to the health benefits claimed for them: more efficient digestion, a build-up of natural

defences and an improved feeling of well-being. At the same time, products enriched with prebiotics (which occur naturally in foods such as bananas, onions and Jerusalem artichokes) began to appear. These acted to stimulate the growth of bacterial probiotics.

A healthy heart

Another lucrative niche for healthfood was the prevention of cardiovascular disease. Medical research had shown the need to rebalance the different types of fatty substances consumed, given that many popular foods, such as meat and dairy products, were too rich in saturated fatty acids while being poor in polyunsaturated fatty acids like Omega-3 and Omega-6, which come from seafood and vegetables. Omega-3s, which the human body cannot synthesise, was particularly deficient in the Western diet but found to be especially good as an anti-inflammatory and for reducing the risk of coronary thrombosis, among other plus points.

Between 1997 and 1999 the market in oils, margarines and yogurts containing Omega-3 and Omega-6 skyrocketed. Research during the 2000s suggested that Omega-3s played a beneficial role in the immune system, cancer prevention and even cognitive disorders, further boosting the market. In Europe the first spread enriched with plant sterols was authorised for production in 2000. The European Commission then went on to sanction the manufacture of a range of sauces, dairy

YOGURT AGAINST ECZEMA

Research in Finland in 2003 showed that a regular dose of 'friendly' gut bacteria – the probiotic lactobacillus GG in yogurts – given to pregnant women helped reduce the risk of their offspring developing atopic eczema, a hereditary skin condition.

products and drinks containing soya, on condition that the supplements they contained did not exceed 3 grams in any single daily portion as recommended on the label.

And yet the jury is still out on whether food supplements have any benefits at all. Firstly, industrial production of foodstuffs does not necessarily reflect the findings obtained under laboratory conditions, and the promise of health benefits, when translated into advertising copy, may turn out to be misleading. Secondly, non-scientific claims on the reduction of cholesterol are often inaccurate. Fats contain two different cholesterols, one of which (HDL, or High Density Lipoprotein) is essential for life and the formation of healthy nerve cells, while the other (LDL, or Low Density Lipoprotein) is largely responsible for the formation of atheromas (blockages) in the circulatory system. These two types, 'good' and 'bad' cholesterol, are frequently confused in claims about cholesterol reduction. Finally, individual factors such as genetic predisposition to certain illnesses, lifestyle choices and occupational hazards can all reduce or negate the anticipated health benefits of modified foodstuffs.

Fuelling the day
It has long been claimed that breakfast is the most important meal of the day. It may constitute as much as 25 per cent of a person's daily food intake. This is why food manufacturers are so keen to sell a range of multivitamin-enriched fruit juices, milk with enhanced iron and calcium content, and energy-giving cereals.

Sprouting goodness
When seeds such as alfalfa and mustard germinate, they become 'living' once more. The sprouts are rich in vitamin C and have a high concentration of micronutrients.

STUDYING BACTERIAL FLORA

Inaugurated in 2008, the European research project called MetaHIT (META genomics of the Human Intestinal Tract) is designed to study the genome of microorganisms that make up our intestinal flora. By comparing microbial communities present in different individuals, in both poor and good health, it will be possible to discover correlations between what people eat, the composition of their intestinal flora and their state of health. This in turn will aid the development of prebiotics and probiotics.

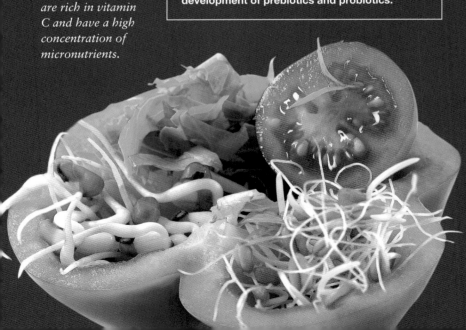

Ever more choice

Functional foods gained acceptance in the 2000s. Supermarket shelves began to fill with fibre-rich products such as fruit juices, yogurts and breakfast cereals promoted as good for the digestion, or for regulating levels of sugar or blood cholesterol. Products with soy isoflavones are claimed to promote circulatory good health and help to guard against cancers. Other innovations are on the drawing board: for instance, the food industry and plant geneticists are collaborating in the development of fruits and vegetables with a higher vitamin content, although this is still very much at the experimental stage.

Aside from modified foodstuffs, the vogue for healthy eating has also seen a rise in the consumption of certain foods or beverages that fit the image of a healthy lifestyle, such as green tea, ginseng and guarana, and of natural, 'unadulterated' products such as wheatgerm, beansprouts and seaweed.

USB sticks 2000

Power supply +5V

Flash memory chip

Management of data input to memory

USB transmission control (USB protocol management)

Power supply +0V

USB connector

Data exchange in parallel transmission

Data exchange in serial transmission

In the annals of inventions that have revolutionised data storage, pride of place today must go to the USB, or Universal Serial Bus. Made as small as practicably possible, this device plugs into a dedicated port on a PC or Mac, and makes data transfer a very simple and quick operation. Developed by, among others, Trek Technology and IBM, this computer peripheral first appeared in 2000. It originally comprised a microchip with flash drive (rewritable memory) of 32MB connected to a male USB connector plug. The capacity has continued to grow since, with the flash memory being replaced by mini hard disk technology. By 2006 the storage limit on this handy little stick had increased to 64GB; by 2010 it was 256GB, equivalent to almost 180,000 floppies, although initially such high-capacity devices had a price-tag of £600 or more. Design departments of different companies have created a huge variety of shapes and colours for their USB sticks.

Transfer and save

USB sticks are ideal for transferring files between computers. From music clips to videos, from business documents to entire operating systems, a USB can hold whatever the user wishes and be plugged into any computer. Yet while it has the advantage of being able to save, copy or back up data quickly, it can also pass on viruses or be used as a way of surreptitiously downloading unauthorised information from a computer.

A spin-off from the USB stick is the 3G stick, which contains a SIM card. This effectively turns it into a mobile phone, enabling the computer it is plugged into to connect to the Internet via the 3G mobile network. In 2009 the KtoK (Key to Key) stick arrived, allowing users to transfer files direct from one USB to another thanks to a dual connector plug and special software.

THE WORLD'S SMALLEST USB DRIVE

Barely larger than a fingernail, the iDisk Diamond manufactured by the Japanese Pretec Corporation has truly minuscule proportions, measuring just 27mm x 12mm x 1.9mm and weighing just 1 gram. Its capacity is limited to 128 MB. Its inventor claims that it is the world's smallest USB data storage solution.

Communication tool

The transmission control circuit inside a USB stick serves as an interface between the flash memory of the stick and the host computer. More than just a simple data transfer tool, the USB stick is a translation device that enables the two entities to communicate with one another without any need for installing software.

The digital notebook 2001

Every sheet of paper in a digital notebook is covered with an invisible, extremely fine coded framework of tiny dots: in total, 700,000 dots, each measuring 0.1mm in diameter, make up each page. These dots act as so many sensors, picking up the trace made by the digital pen and transferring the coordinates to a software application installed in the user's computer via either a USB or a wireless connection. The writing is then retranscribed onto the computer screen. Digital notebooks represent a coming together of four separate technologies: a camera, coordinate system reference from the paper, handwriting recognition and data transfer mechanisms.

Handwritten office automation

In 1995 Christian Fahraeus, a microbiology student at the University of Lund in Sweden, came up with the idea for a pen that could read text: the so-called C-pen contained a digital camera, a fast microprocessor and image-processing software. A first prototype appeared in 1997 manufactured by Anoto, a company that Fahraeus set up. But at this stage the C-pen still lacked any 'smart' data-collection system. In 2001 the Swede unveiled his Anoto Pattern process, which enabled the pen to recognise its precise position on the page. This breakthrough signalled the birth of the electronic notebook.

In the same year, building on the technology devised at Anoto, the Hamelin stationery company in Oxford brought out the first mass-market digital notebook, which it named the Easybook. In 2004 a French rival, Clairefontaine (Exacompta), in partnership with Metalinks, launched its own digital notebook, the PaperPC. Further development work by Kayentis (2006) and MG Stream (2008) saw the introduction of notebooks designed for professional use. Nevertheless, digital notebooks are primarily used today by the general and educational market. They are an ideal way for school pupils or students to capture information electronically through handwriting in situations where it is impractical to take notes using a keyboard.

Notes on the go
The Anoto Pattern (right) is not so very different from a conventional notepad, yet every movement of the pen is registered by a camera. This is then reproduced in digital form in the computer as though it has scanned the text and converted into an electronic file.

Technological marvel
The pen used for digital notebooks is a minor masterpiece of modern technology. It comprises an ink cartridge, a battery, a pressure sensor, a digital camera that records how many dots on a paper pattern have been covered, a microprocessor and flash memory.

DIGITAL NOTEBOOK USES

The ability to create any type of office document from notes written down on a digital notebook opens up a whole range of possibilities. For instance, the written data can be transferred to a computer or a mobile phone, sent via e-mail or text message, or stored and archived. Future applications of this roaming electronic notepad technology might include interactive journalism, where a response could be sent simply by clicking with the pen on an article, or in medicine, with doctors being able to update patients' notes remotely.

Knowledge at your fingertips

Online encyclopedias and digital libraries have made the world of learning accessible to all, at any time of day. All users need to do to access this fund of knowledge is to browse the immense resources of the World Wide Web and select the information they require.

In order to research a report, examine a rare manuscript or find a quotation, all you have to do today is type the search keyword into an Internet search engine, such as Google, then follow the links to the sites that come up. The first entry may well direct you to Wikipedia, the free online encyclopedia founded in 2001 on the initiative of Americans Larry Sanger and Jimmy Wales. Hypertext links and extensive indexing of works online might send you to Google Books. By 2010 this digital library, which was conceived in 2004 as a spin-off for the world's leading search engine, contained almost 10 million digitised books, both ancient and modern, ranging from scholarly treatises to cookery books. Depending on what information is sought, the Internet surfer can consult extracts of books or works in their entirety before seeking out a hard copy in a real library, or alternatively downloading it from the Web.

All manner of libraries

The first online library in the world was the Gutenberg, which to date has made more than 30 million titles available in over 40 languages, in the main literary classics that have lapsed from copyright and so are in the public domain. Back in 1971, Gutenberg's founder Michael Hart foresaw the possibility that computers would transcend their original function of doing calculations and become a virtual book repository offering storage, research and browsing facilities. A student at the University of Illinois at the time, Hart made the first digitised texts available to users of the IT network on the college campus. Project Gutenberg really came into its own, though, with the advent of the World Wide Web.

Major institutions such as the British Library, Massachusetts Institute of Technology (MIT) and the Bibliothèque Nationale de France

Seat of learning
The US National Library of Congress (below), founded in Washington, DC, in 1800 is the world's largest library by number of works held, with almost 142 million documents. Digitisation of its holdings began in 2001.

DIGITAL DATA CAPTURE

Books and magazines can be transformed into electronic documents or digitised in image mode by using a scanner. Because the pages that appear on the screen are identical to the originals, this method of data capture was initially preferred by the large institutional libraries. But a scanned document is a read-only resource. To capture a document in text mode, two further stages are required: reading the target file with a piece of optical character recognition (OCR) software, followed by a re-reading – and correction if need be – of the file produced by the OCR program. Despite huge progress in this field, the software still makes mistakes, especially when reading very old texts. Project Gutenberg and its counterpart Wikisource (managed by the same foundation that runs Wikipedia) rely on volunteers to make any necessary corrections. As text mode enables a text to be indexed, searched and analysed, institutional libraries are investing more and more in OCR treatment of documents.

(BNF) began digitising their collections towards the end of the 1980s with an eye to conserving what were in some cases very fragile resources. An integral part of this process saw them publish their catalogues and make available a growing portion of their holdings for remote research on the Web. Free access resources include the World Digital Library (2009), an initiative by UNESCO to make rare books and manuscripts, maps, photographs, films and sound archives available in seven languages; Europeana (2010), an EU venture involving 100 museums, libraries and archives; and Gallica, launched by the BNF in 1997.

Homework help
A 2006 study found that 98 per cent of children in the UK had access to the Internet, with the most frequent use being research for school projects.

THE BIRTH OF GOOGLE

In 1995 two IT whizz-kids, Larry Page and Sergey Brin, met on the campus of Stanford University in California. They hit it off immediately and together began developing their PageRank technology, a system for classifying Web pages that would go on to form the core of the most successful search engine on the Internet. Their start-up company Google, which they founded in 1998, had a meteoric rise. It made a huge splash when floated on Wall Street in 2004, and is now one of an elite group of hugely rich and powerful multinationals.

Expertise in a mouseclick

Encyclopedias are another domain that has been enriched by the Internet. In 1998 the Canadian philosopher Jacques Dufresne set up the Agora encyclopedia, the first such online resource, which appeared in French. Agora offered easy access, constant updating of content, and an interactive facility that allowed contributors and users alike to post comments on the forums.

But it is Wikipedia – the name comes from the Hawaiian *wiki*, meaning 'quick' – which has exploited the possibilities of the Web to the full. Volunteers are responsible for writing, modifying, checking and updating the articles and providing footnotes on this huge and continually growing online encyclopedia. In less than ten years since its inception, almost a million people have had a hand in creating or amending some 40 million separate articles available in 270 different languages. The English version, with a million articles, is the most significant branch of Wikipedia, closely followed by the French and German sites with 700,000 articles apiece. Overall, Wikipedia ranks as the fifth most visited site worldwide.

The phenomenon of online encyclopedias caught traditional publishers of these resources off guard. To offset falling sales, respected and well-established encyclopedias in Germany (Brockhaus) and France (Larousse) decided to put their works on the Internet. Unlike Wikipedia, the articles here are still written by accredited experts and the sites are funded by advertising revenue; Larousse puts amateur articles alongside the entries written by the professionals. The American publisher of the *Encyclopedia Britannica* initially put the vast work online in its entirety for free, but access to full articles is now restricted to subscribers.

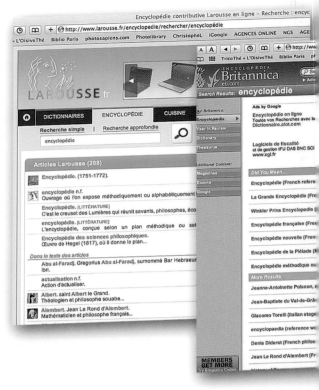

Multilingual resource
At the latest count there were 282 different language versions of the multilingual Wikipedia. The English version has the greatest number of articles, followed by German and then French (below). It is the only educational website that is consistently near the top of the 'most visited' list. One of its founding principles was that its content should be freely modifiable by users and can therefore be constantly improved.

IS WIKIPEDIA RELIABLE?

Contrary to the general belief that Wikipedia is full of inaccuracies, comparative analyses by academics suggest that the level of errors found in Wikipedia articles is not significantly higher than that in traditional encyclopedia entries. But it was the case that biased or false information was removed more quickly from articles on sensitive subjects, which received the most hits, than it was from other entries. Knowledge was also deemed to be skewed in terms of excessive emphasis on popular or topical subjects. Coverage of scientific disciplines was also thought to be patchy or lacking in analysis and context.

Organising knowledge

In 2006 Larry Sanger, one of the founders of Wikipedia, launched a new online encyclopedia called Citizendium. In response to the charge of unreliability levelled at Wikipedia, the contributors to Citizendium are named and their entries are peer-reviewed by a panel of experts who are responsible for editing and organising the content. The larger question arising from this is how best to structure a coherent body of knowledge within a dynamic, changing medium like the Internet, where the preponderance of ephemera works against permanence or stability. It seems that virtual libraries and encyclopedias can reclaim the mediating role that their real-life counterparts have always played, acting as arbiters of reliable knowledge.

Most of the rival sites to Wikipedia and Google enable users, in addition to searching by keyword, to navigate by subject area, theme, period, type of document and/or geographical location. Notes edited by specialists and appended to documents in the World Digital Library help visitors find their bearings and access other articles of interest. Other sites provide hints on further reading for the chosen subject. The European Library forms a link between the digitised resources of 48 national libraries the length and breadth of Europe.

Software developers use the term 'Web 2.0' to describe applications that allow participatory information-sharing and collaboration, though it does not denote any technical upgrade. One important technological innovation on the horizon is the so-called 'Semantic Web'. Using a language called Resource Description Framework (RDF), this will effectively make Web applications more intelligent, enabling them to gather and combine information from many different sources, and present it to users in a meaningful way. Internet searches will thus become much more targeted and sophisticated than ever before.

Universal knowledge
A selection of Web pages from online encyclopedias in French, English and German. One advantage these resources have over their paper equivalents is the wealth of hypertext links for the user to explore.

AUTHORS' RIGHTS

In Europe and the USA, creative works are protected by the right to intellectual property for a period of up to 70 years on average after the death of the author. Consequently, they cannot be distributed over the Internet without the permission of the author during his or her lifetime, or of their legal beneficiary during the period when copyright is still in force. Thereafter, they lapse into the public domain and can be used and reproduced by anyone. The digitisation of contemporary works by Google has sparked a legal battle between the company on the one hand and editors and authors on the other. Aside from the debate over the rights of authors, critics of Google point to the danger of allowing the world's cultural heritage to be made subservient to the commercial interests of a dominant multinational organisation.

Tools to help police with their enquiries

Science can help criminal investigators to uncover the truth. A single hair, a scrap of clothing or a drop of saliva are enough to convict or exonerate a defendant. From DNA analysis to decryption of mobile phone chips, via ballistics, toxicology and the study of explosives, the gamut of sophisticated forensic techniques is capable of gleaning a huge amount of information from the faintest clues and samples collected during an enquiry.

Genetic crimefighting
A laboratory assistant at a forensic facility (left) taking a sample of bloodstained clothing to test for DNA. So-called DNA 'fingerprinting' has revolutionised the fight against crime, although there is a tiny chance of misidentification.

War on terror
French forensics experts (below) pick over the scene of a bomb blast. Scientific police work is vital in determining what type of explosives were used and how a bomb was detonated. Such details can help in the hunt for the perpetrators.

'Wherever he steps, whatever he touches, whatever he leaves, even without consciousness, will serve as a silent witness against him.' *Silent Witness*, the long-running and popular BBC television drama series about the work of forensic pathologists, took its title from this quotation from a 1953 American textbook on the police laboratory. But the principle enshrined in the quotation was developed by a Frenchman, Dr Edmond Locard, in the early decades of the 20th century. It is thanks to Locard that modern crime investigation bureaus incorporate scientific departments dedicated to gathering and examining physical evidence. Be it a crime of passion, an armed bank robbery or a terrorist bomb exploding in a tube station, the

LE LABORATOIRE CENTRAL
PERMANENCE GENERALE

POLICE
TECHNIQUE
&
SCIENTIFIQUE

POLICE
TECHNIQUE
&
SCIENTIFIQUE

Small beginnings
A body outline, drawn in chalk, at the scene of a killing: such rudimentary methods used to characterise police work. Nowadays, considerable resources are devoted the world over to forensic science, using the most sophisticated techniques.

first investigators on the scene are the specialist scientific agents led by a crime scene manager.

Gathering the evidence

These highly skilled police technicians – familiar from many TV series besides *Silent Witness*, such as *Waking the Dead* and the American shows *CSI* and *NCIS* ('Naval Criminal Investigation Service') – appear in garb worthy of a hospital operating theatre: disposable overalls, hair nets, face masks, latex gloves and plastic overshoes. They then

Public fascination
A scene from the hit US television series CSI: Crime Scene Investigation *(right). Long-running shows like this have helped to highlight the work of police forensic teams, albeit in glamorised form.*

FRANCE'S REAL SHERLOCK HOLMES

Edmond Locard (1877–1966) is widely regarded as the founding father of forensic science. After studying medicine and law at Lyons, in 1910 he persuaded the police department there to turn two small rooms into the world's first crime laboratory. In his *Manual of Police Techniques* (1923), he set out what later became known as 'Locard's exchange principle': 'It is impossible for a criminal to act, especially considering the intensity of a crime, without leaving traces of this presence.' Georges Simenon, author of the famous *Maigret* detective novels, attended Locard's lectures.

set about photographing and sketching the cordoned-off crime scene, aiming to capture it in the exact state they found it. Infinite care is taken in identifying fingerprints by means of special UV lamps, then lifing them with powder applied with paintbrushes. Every possible sample is collected – blood, sperm, gunshot residue, bullet fragments, glass, paint, drugs, textile fibres, chewing-gum, cigarette butts, even insects and pollen. Finally, they make imprints of footprints, tyre marks and any bite marks on bodies.

Once the scene has been thoroughly gone over with a fine-tooth comb, a substance is applied that has proved invaluable for revealing traces of blood invisible to the human eye: luminol, a luminescent compound that reacts to the presence of certain elements such as metallic ions. Since haemoglobin contains iron, all that is needed is to crush some luminol, dilute it in

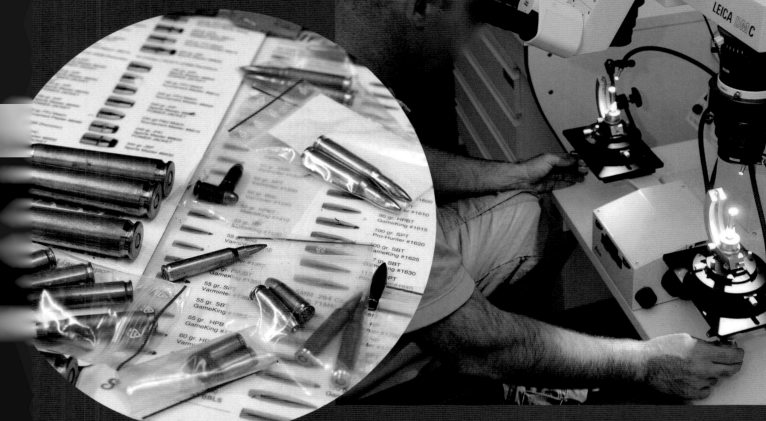

an alkaline solution with oxygenated water and spread it over a surface contaminated with blood, where it reacts with the iron and emits a bluish glow. Even a drop of blood diluted 1:1,000 parts can be detected in this way.

Breakthroughs in ballistics

If a firearm is recovered, the first thing to be determined back at the lab is whether the gun is definitely the murder weapon. To do this, a ballistics expert will use it to fire a practice round; if the rifling marks on the bullet casing match those on the bullets found at the scene, its identity is confirmed. Rifling marks are striations on the casing made by the projectile's passage down the gun barrel, where it rubs against spiral grooves on the inside. If bullets and spent cartridge cases are all that is found, the ballistics team, who have a huge array of firearms at their disposal, examine these marks to find out what type of gun was used

Tracing the murder weapon
A range of different calibre bullets in a police forensic lab (above left). Every firearm produces a unique mark when discharged. When cartridge cases are examined under a comparison macroscope (above right), distinctive tell-tale signs such as breach marks, firing pin impressions and rifling patterns come to light. This device is a key tool in forensics.

Working from parameters like the point of impact and the nature of the wounds on victims' bodies, they can accurately reconstruct and model in 3D the path of the projectiles to and through their target, then work out where the shooter was standing.

FORENSIC GEOPHYSICS

In investigating and locating objects or features hidden underground – a corpse buried in concrete, say, or an arms cache – forensic scientists have a vital new tool in the form of ground-penetrating radar (GPR). Looking something like a cross between a pushchair and a lawn mower, this device emits high-frequency radar pulses that penetrate the soil; if they encounter an anomaly, the pulses are reflected back to the surface. Geophysics proved vital in the case of the notorious Gloucester serial killer Fred West in 1994.

DNA fingerprinting

In recent times, many cases have been solved through the application of 'genetic fingerprinting'. More precisely, a molecular technique known as polymerase chain reaction (PCR) is used to amplify a specific portion of DNA, however tiny, from organic traces found at the crime scene in order to produce a large number of nearly identical copies for analysis. From this material, biologists can decipher all or part of the genome of cells present in a spot of saliva, say, or a drop of blood or sperm, or from hair, skin or dandruff samples. These are then compared against hundreds of thousands of genetic fingerprints stored on a database. If the genetic profile of the suspect corresponds to one of the profiles already on record, the individual can be immediately identified. Automated genotyping units, which analyse all the reference samples from an individual on a kind of conveyor belt holding microplates, mean that the results are available within a day, rather than the several days required if all the operations are carried out by hand.

Different disciplines

A wide spectrum of scientific disciplines has been brought into play to aid forensic work. For example, botanists can provide invaluable data: the study of diatoms, the microscopic algae found in all bodies of water, can enable a coroner to pronounce a verdict of death by drowning – or not as the case may be. For if water entered the victim's bloodstream before

DOG DETECTIVES

Even if criminals take great care to leave no fingerprints or traces of DNA at the crime scene, they can still be betrayed by body odour. The technique was pioneered by the notorious Stasi secret police in the former German Democratic Republic for tracking political dissidents. Some jurisdictions have since adopted it in the fight against crime. Samples of odours taken from the suspect or their possessions using cotton swabs are placed in hermetically sealed jars. A trained sniffer dog is given these to smell, and then released into a room containing jars of swabs, one of which was collected at the crime scene, while the others are random control samples. If the dog correctly matches the suspect's smell with the crime-scene odour, the jars are switched around and the test repeated. If the dog consistently chooses this same jar, the tests are run again using another dog as a double-check.

Incontrovertible evidence
DNA profiling is now one of the principal strategies in the fight against crime. DNA is retrieved from saliva left on cigarette butts (left), chewing gum, hair or other organic material. The genetic profile obtained is stored on a database.

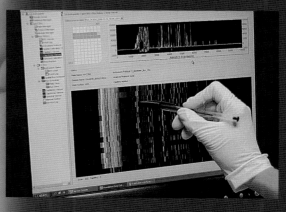

Keeping tabs
In England and Wales, profiles of convicted criminals are kept indefinitely on the UK National Criminal Intelligence DNA database. Other profiles are removed after 6 or 12 years, depending on the gravity of the suspected offence.

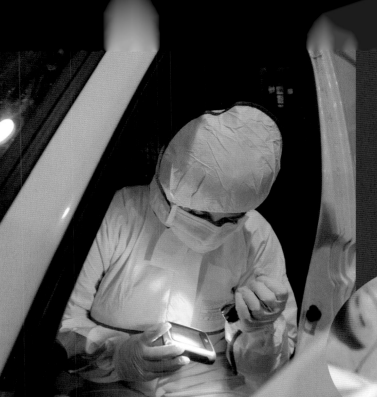

Dactyloscopy in action
A fingerprint analyst taking samples of greasy finger imprints, invisible to the naked eye, left on a car (left). To stand up in court, two fingerprints must have 12 characteristic features in common (below) and no differences.

and then combination, often unique, is entered into an international database constantly updated by manufacturers. Likewise, enlarging the filament of a headlamp bulb under an electron microscope can reveal if it was broken when it was hot or cold – in other words, whether the headlamps of a car involved in an accident were lit at the time or not.

Drugs and death

In cases of poisoning, toxicologists are called in to ascertain what toxins, drugs or medication were involved. In drugs seizures, they analyse what chemicals have been used to synthesise heroin, ecstasy or cocaine, and this can point detectives towards particular suppliers in illegal drug 'factories' who are known to use specific compounds.

Identifying a body and determining the cause of death is another essential forensic task. Intensive study of human remains, involving analysis of bone trauma, dentition and sometimes even facial reconstruction can enable investigators to put a name to a corpse that has decomposed or been burned beyond recognition. Forensic entomology, the study of insects in and around a decomposing cadaver, can help place the time of death extremely accurately.

Digital detection

Many cases have been solved by investigating mobile phone SIM cards to find out whom a suspect called, and exactly when, in the hours or days leading up to a crime, and what was discussed. Even when a mobile has been

the heart stopped beating, then diatoms will occur throughout the body, whereas if the person was put in the water already dead, the diatoms only appear in the lungs. Depending on what different species of aquatic microorganism turn up in the corpse, the experts can ascertain whether or not the drowning took place at the spot where the victim's body was discovered.

Palynologists bring to bear on criminology their knowledge of hundreds of different species of listed plants. In this way pollen grains recovered from a crime scene or the clothes of a suspect can be vital clues. In Austria in 1969, a killer with a clear motive but who could not be placed at the crime scene was convicted through forensic palynology: mud on a pair of his boots was found to contain a fossil hickory pollen present only at the location where the murder took place.

Incriminating scrape
An international criminal database called the Paint Data Query (PDQ) allows forensic scientists to identify and trace suspect vehicles from the minutest samples of bodywork paint.

Trapped by traces

Explosives, inflammable materials, shards of glass, metal and paint undergo physical and chemical analysis using tchniques such as chromatography, spectrometry and scanning electron microscopy. For instance, a microscopic trace of paint left by a vehicle after a collision is enough to trace the make, model and even the year of construction of a car. All cellulose paint on car bodywork is in four layers: an electrophoretic coating, a primer, a coloured basecoat and a clearcoat veneer. Each layer has its own characteristics,

PLAYING IT BY EAR

Voice recognition technology is still in its early stages and, in most jurisdictions, tape recordings are only admissible as evidence under strictly controlled conditions. The problem is that a voice is not reliably identifiable as belonging to a particular individual: a voice can be disguised – as professional impressionists regularly demonstrate – if surveillance is suspected. However, the FBI has been trialling software called FASR ('Forensic Automatic Speaker Recognition') that could make a person's voice as uniquely identifiable as their fingerprints. It was used, for instance, to tell whether audio recordings supposedly made by Osama bin Laden between 2001 and 2011 were genuine.

deliberately destroyed to try to conceal the evidence, experts can retrieve vital information by unsoldering the microchips and decoding them using special reading devices.

Similarly, computer hard drives are minutely dissected and the files that their former owners thought they had erased are resurrected. Cyberdetectives also regularly visit certain sites and messageboards, to try to track down people who assume false identities in order to groom minors for sex. The advent of widespread public CCTV has also furnished investigators

with a huge amount of footage on which perpetrators may be shown.

Clearly, this type of police work would soon become unmanageable without technological aids. Law enforcement agencies are currently involved in developing software that can select all the faces appearing on video footage and rearrange them within seconds into a sort of still photo album. This will save investigators untold time sifting through hours of footage, and should also help them to instantly locate, say, a lost child in a shopping mall or produce hard evidence of a drug pusher who denies having met such-and-such a dealer in such-and-such a train station.

Plain to see
To detect prints on a porous surface, the sample to be analysed is first soaked in a chemical bath. It is then dried before being scanned with a CrimeScope, a hand-held laser that reveals fingerprints and other body fluids unseen by the naked eye.

FUTURE FANTASY

Steven Spielberg's 2002 film *Minority Report*, from a novel by American science-fiction writer Philip K Dick, is set in the America of 2054, where murder has been eradicated thanks to three humans called 'Precogs' with special powers of foresight. Based at the Ministry of Justice, these individuals detect signs of homicidal acts of violence that are about to be committed and beam their mental images to a specialised police unit, Precrime, which steps in to prevent the crime. All pure fantasy: the role of the neurosciences in crimefighting is still in its infancy. Even so, scientists do not rule out the possibility of one day being able to gauge the chances of a person committing a crime from their brainwave patterns.

Fly me to the Moon

On 28 April, 2001, US businessman Dennis Tito became the world's first 'space tourist'. Thanks to an arrangement between the private companies MirCorp and Space Adventures, after a training period at the Russian Baikonur cosmodrome Tito was sent into orbit on a Soyuz spacecraft. Disembarking aboard the ISS (International Space Station), he spent 7 days, 22 hours and 4 minutes in space, orbiting the Earth 128 times.

Space Adventures, founded in 1998, is now the only private enterprise offering the public trips into space. To do this, it rents spaces from the Russian Federation aboard their Soyuz craft, launched from Baikonur in Kazakhstan. Space Adventures employs a consultative committee of former astronauts, including Buzz Aldrin, the second man to walk on the Moon in 1969. Its portfolio includes a range of space-related activities, such as taking authentic cosmonaut training and practising on Soyuz simulators, but its greatest success has been its orbital flights; by the end of 2009, it had organised seven such trips. In April 2002 Mark Shuttleworth became the first African to go into space; he trained for the mission for 8 months at NASA's Johnson Space Center in Houston, Texas. And in September 2006 the American-Iranian Anousheh Ansari, a successful businesswoman, became the first female space tourist. Ansari stayed on the ISS for eight days, conducting medical and physiological experiments on behalf of the

European Space Agency (ESA). As for Charles Simonyi, he was the first space tourist to make the trip twice, while Guy Laliberté was the first Canadian space tourist. Apart from Laliberté, who is the founder of the world-renowned alternative circus Cirque du Soleil, all the other space tourists made their fortunes in the IT or communications industry. For the time being, and probably for some considerable time into the future, orbiting the Earth on a spacecraft will remain the preserve of a handful of rich individuals who are able and willing to spend around $20 million per journey.

Suborbital flight

At a lower altitude, but far less expensive, suborbital flight seems destined to become the main vehicle for space travel that is accessible to a wider public. Its development has been promoted by the founding of the X Prize, renamed the Ansari X Prize in 2004 in recognition of a donation of several million dollars by Anousheh and Amir Ansari.

Happy man
Dennis Tito (centre), a former NASA engineer, on the International Space Station (ISS). Tito almost missed out on being the first paying astronaut when the Russian space station Mir, where he was due to stay, was taken out of commission and deorbited on 23 March, 2001, just weeks before his departure.

Up and away!
A Soyuz space capsule takes off from Baikonur on 25 April, 2002 (above), headed for the ISS. Taking part in the mission was Flight Participant Mark Shuttleworth, a South African space tourist; his country's flag appears on the rocket's nose-cone. The mission conducted several scientific experiments on AIDS and the human genome.

Getting ready
Space tourist Guy Laliberté in training at the Star City cosmonaut training centre, a former military complex near Moscow.

THE 'VOMIT COMET'

A more cost-effective way of experiencing some of the effects of zero-gravity spaceflight is to take a trip on one of the aircraft that NASA use to acclimatise their astronauts to mission conditions. These specially converted airliners, in which all the seats are removed and the floors and walls padded, fly switchback 'parabolic' trajectories, which render the passengers weightless for periods of 20 seconds or so. Because of the disorienting effect such violent manoeuvres can have on the body, the aircraft are nicknamed the 'Vomit Comets'. The eminent British physicist Stephen Hawking took one of these flights in 2007, and BBC popular science presenter James May followed suit in 2009 in preparation for an upper-atmosphere flight in a U2 spy plane.

Inaugurated in 1996, the competition offered a prize of US $10 million to the first private enterprise to launch a reusable spacecraft to the edge of space twice within the space of two weeks. The edge of space was defined as an altitude of 100 kilometres: beyond this point weightlessness kicks in, allowing a person to float, free from Earth's gravitational pull.

The prize was won on 4 October, 2004 – the 47th anniversary to the day of the launch of Sputnik 1 – by the experimental craft *SpaceShipOne*, which lifted off for the second time from Mojave Airport in the Nevada Desert, California. Built with financial backing from Paul Allen, one of the co-founders of Microsoft, the machine is 8 metres long, weighs 1.2 tonnes unladen and can carry three passengers. *SpaceShipOne* began its flight slung under the belly of another machine, the *White Knight* carrier aircraft, which in 50 minutes took it up to an altitude of 15 kilometres. *SpaceShipOne* was then released into a few seconds of free fall, before its rocket motors ignited for an 80-second burst. Running on a mixture of solid and liquid propellants for greater reliability, the engines enabled it to reach speeds of Mach 3, or 1,000m/sec. *SpaceShipOne*, which is the only private aircraft capable of such speed, soared briefly into the lower reaches of space, where it stayed for a few minutes before returning to earth like a conventional plane.

Shooting for the stars

Impressive though they are, the exploits of *SpaceShipOne* cannot meet the needs of space

New era in flight
Slung below its mother ship White Knight, *SpaceShipOne makes its maiden flight from Mojave Airport on 29 September, 2004 (right). The first privately funded American craft to reach space, the composite aircraft was built by Scaled Composites, a company under the direction of veteran aviator Burt Rutan.*

Anousheh Ansari – blasting off at 40
Just days after her 40th birthday, Ansari (above) became the first female space tourist. During six months of training she learned Russian and familiarised herself with the Soyuz *capsule.*

tourism. There are too few places on board and conditions are too cramped. A new craft, *SpaceShipTwo*, was unveiled in 2009 and made its maiden flight in October 2010. It is currently undergoing trials with the aim of launching commercial operations in 2012, run by the Virgin Galactic spaceline, an offshoot of Sir Richard Branson's Virgin travel and media empire. More than 300 people have already reserved tickets at an average cost of around £120,000. *SpaceShipTwo* will carry two pilots and six passengers. Like its predecessor, it will piggy-back to high altitude on a mother ship, *White Knight Two*, before being released to cruise up and skim the frontier of space. The passengers will be able to enjoy the experience of weightlessness for six minutes. In honour of the popular, long-running sci-fi series Star Trek, the first two *SpaceShipTwo* modules will be called VSS *Enterprise* and VSS *Voyager*.

In total, the Virgin Galactic fleet will comprise two *White Knight Two* carrier planes and five spaceplanes. In addition to tourism, the company plans to conduct scientific missions and launch small telecommunications and remote detection satellites.

Space hub of the future?
An artist's impression of the projected 'Spaceport America' in the New Mexico desert. Work on this, the world's first airport dedicated to suborbital spaceflight, began on 19 June, 2009. It is the latest venture of entrepreneur Richard Branson, who pays an indemnity of US $1 million a year to retain freehold of the site. On 18 October, 2011, Branson was joined by astronaut Buzz Aldrin at the terminal-hangar for the dedication ceremony. With the spaceport and mothership completed, the company is now finalising its rocket tests.

High flyer
SpaceShipOne *gliding gracefully after being released at high altitude by its carrier craft. On 17 December, 2003, the centenary of the Wright Brothers' first controlled powered flight, SpaceShipOne became the first private craft to venture to the lower limits of space.*

IN TRANSIT TO THE STARS

Spaceport America, 140km north of El Paso in the desert of New Mexico, will be the first facility dedicated to suborbital space tourism. The facility is owned by Virgin Galactic and It is from here that their spaceplanes will take off. Construction of the futuristic and ecological building, designed to conjure up the thrill of space travel, has been entrusted to the partnership of the British architect Sir Norman Foster. But because much of the interest being shown in space tourism is coming from the oil-rich Middle East, construction of two more such facilities is planned for the United Arab Emirates – one for Virgin near Abu Dhabi, the other outside Dubai for the Space Adventures company. As of 2010, debate was still ongoing about where to site a European spaceport.

While Virgin currently finds itself at the forefront of the space tourism business, it will surely not be long before serious competition emerges. Space Adventures, for instance, is planning to offer similar trips on board *Explorer*, a suborbital vehicle capable of carrying five passengers, which the company is developing jointly with the Russian Space Agency. This craft will also be launched into space from a carrier plane and, for just over 100,000 dollars apiece, will provide its passengers with five minutes of weightlessness.

Over the Moon

SpaceShipThree was originally planned to be a fully orbital vehicle, but Virgin Galactic revised the specification and now envisage it as a kind of super-Concorde that could fly from London to Sydney in just two hours. Even so, the future of space tourism is thought to lie in orbital flight. Space Adventures is already offering stays of six days on the ISS, with the possibility of venturing out on a space walk, an experience only a very few professional astronauts and cosmonauts have been fortunate enough to experience. Plus, for 100 million dollars, a genuine Moon mission could take tourists on a 45-minute excursion over the surface of the Moon.

HOTELS IN SPACE

Building hotels in space is not as crazy a venture at it might sound. Robert Bigelow, founder of a chain of hotels in the United States and head of the Bigelow Aerospace company, has already had two inflatable space living modules launched from Russia – Genesis I in 2006 and Genesis II in 2007 – in order to test the long-term viability of this kind of structure. The problem is not the spaciousness of the accommodation, but the surroundings. In December 2006, Genesis I was buffeted by a solar tempest, a flow of particles thrown out by the Sun, which almost put it out of action. This served as a timely reminder that space is a hazardous environment subject to potentially fatal radiation surges. To monitor their effect, the first guests to test the facilities on board Genesis II are cockroaches, scorpions and ants. The objective is to send several of these modules into orbit and link them together to create a hotel floating more than 500km above the Earth. The cost of a room with an unbeatable view of the Earth is projected to be 1 million dollars a night.

Spaceflight attendant
A computer artist's impression of a Virgin Galactic stewardess (top). The spacecraft is based on the SpaceShipOne design. In March 2010 Virgin's SpaceShipTwo, hitched to its mother ship, made a first test flight of almost 3 hours over the Californian desert. On their flights, space tourists will be able to enjoy spectacular views of Earth, as seen from the ISS (above).

A lifesaving stock-take

Ten years after the adoption of the UN Convention on Biological Diversity in 1992, the signatory governments were involved in a desperate attempt to halt the alarming decline in biodiversity before 2010. Scientists are now predicting a sixth mass extinction – this time as a result of human activity – yet the full inventory of the world's species is still far from complete.

The Baiji, or Yangtse river dolphin (*Lipotes vexillifer*) is thought to have already become extinct: ten years after an expedition counted just 13 individuals in the great Chinese waterway, another expedition in 2007 scoured the polluted river in vain for any dolphins. One mammal species in every four could potentially suffer the same fate over the next century, along with one in eight birds and a third of all species of amphibians, according to the International Union for the Conservation of Nature (IUCN). This umbrella organisation brings together governments, NGOs, scientists and volunteer groups from around 160 countries. Since 1963, when it began cataloguing the conservation status of all known animal and plant species, the number of those whose survival in the wild is critically endangered has steadily increased. At the time of writing, 36 per cent of species reviewed are on the IUCN's Red List and endangered to some degree.

Extinction is programmed into the natural course of evolution of species. Furthermore, since the beginnings of life on Earth, there have been five mass extinction events, each of which wiped out between 65 and 95 per cent of all extant species. These mass extinctions were all triggered by global natural disasters. Today, the rate of extinction is a hundred to a thousand times faster, and what experts are already calling the sixth mass extinction is clearly a result of human activity. As the march of the human species continues, growing evermore numerous and urbanised in the process, it relentlessly encroaches on habitats formerly occupied by other living creatures. Excessive hunting or overfishing can destroy wild populations faster than they can reproduce. Elsewhere, humans introduce species that are useful to them, gradually eliminating natural diversity within a particular area.

The tree of life

It is impossible to estimate how many species of plants and animals may have become extinct before humans were even aware of their disappearance. Although scientists have described, named and classified around 1.8 million species, the true figure is thought to be somewhere between 10 and 100 million. Annually, scientific discovery adds some 12,000 new species to the tree of life. Almost two-thirds of these are insects, but mammals, which along with birds are the most

Unique habitat
Cholla cacti in the Joshua Tree National Park in California (above), a desert landscape classified as specially protected wilderness by the IUCN.

Precarious existence
The Amazon river dolphin, Inia geoffrensis *(left), lives in the muddy waters of South America's largest river, where it has no predators other than humans. It is currently one of the three most critically endangered dolphin species in the world.*

well-known and extensively studied life forms, account for 15–20 new discoveries each year.

In recent times, biologists have organised an increasing number of fact-finding expeditions, particularly to those habitats such as tropical rainforests and coral reefs where large numbers of different species congregate. The depths of the world's oceans, which may be home to many unknown species, remain far less accessible. Yet while compiling a complete inventory of vertebrates and flowering plants seems an achievable goal, the same cannot be said for the almost unimaginable numbers of invertebrates and non-flowering plants.

Taking a census of species and identifying them is the first stage in implementing a protection policy. Historically these have focused on three areas: regulating the capture or commercial exploitation of species that have been clearly identified as endangered; the conservation of species in zoos, botanical gardens or seed banks; and protection of habitat. There have been some notable successes: regulation of whale hunting – which began as far back as 1937 and culminated in a ban on all commercial whaling in 1986 – has given some populations the chance to recover, despite the fact that the ban has not been observed by all countries. Likewise, the

Victim of logging
This species of giant dragonfly (left), found only in the jungle of southwestern Cameroon and southeastern Nigeria, is just one of many creatures around the world threatened by clear-felling of trees for lumber.

Slaughtered for profit *Indian customs officials with a haul of poached leopard and tiger skins, seized in Kolkata in 2009. Big cat species are under threat the world over.*

American bison (*Bison bison*), which was almost wiped out in the late 19th century, found a sanctuary in Yellowstone National Park, the first reserve of its kind in the world, established in 1872. Meanwhile, in the 1920s the European bison or wisent (*Bison bonasus*) owed its survival solely to protection measures and captive-breeding programmes. Thirty years later, the first individuals were reintroduced to the forests of Poland. But neither legislation nor the existence of protected areas, which now cover around 12 per cent of the Earth's land surface, can prevent poaching. Above all, traditional protection methods are not sufficiently responsive to the dynamic nature of ecosystems or to human interference in them.

Focus on biodiversity

Advances in the ecological sciences have revealed the complexity of living organisms, as well as the interactions and constant changes that are at work in nature. Since the 1990s, species diversity has no longer been the sole yardstick determining scientific research and the formulation of environmental protection policy. Genetic diversity is now a major consideration, both where the individual species and an entire ecosystem is concerned. Indeed, it is the genetic variability within a population that ensures its capacity to adapt to upheavals in its environment. Within its habitat, a species may maintain a variety of relations with others, including predation, mutualism and parasitism. The notion of biodiversity places the emphasis on the resources feeding into an ecosystem, including

Too tasty to survive?
The numbers of bluefin tuna in the oceans have plummeted. Highly prized for its flesh, which is used raw in Japanese sushi and sashimi dishes, this magnificent creature is a victim of overfishing (above).

Close-run thing
Unrestricted big-game hunting by European settlers almost drove the American bison of the Great Plains to extinction. Luckily these majestic animals were saved by a captive-breeding programme.

DNA – A NEW TOOL IN MEASURING DIVERSITY

Over the last few decades, variations in DNA have supplemented the morphological and behavioural criteria that scientists use to distinguish and classify species. Nowadays, advances in DNA sequencing have raised hopes that the cataloguing of all living species may proceed faster than once feared. For instance, metagenomics can identify all the genes present in a soil or water sample without having to pinpoint individual organisms. This allows researchers to evaluate the level of diversity of this type of environment without first needing to determine in isolation all the species it comprises.

AUDITING BIODIVERSITY

We can quantify the value of, say, a tree cut down in an equatorial rainforest, or of the horn of a white rhinoceros poached from a national park. But what price can be put on the benefits accruing from biodiversity? According to the first study in this field, published in 2009 by the international TEEB programme ('The Economics of Ecosystems and Biodiversity', established in 2007 at the instigation of the European Commission), on a global scale this figure can be set at roughly 14,000 billion dollars. The calculation took into account such things as crop pollination by bees and the 'price' of a rainforest, the latter obtained by asking a sample of people what imports they would be prepared to forgo in order to save it from destruction. TEEB's conclusion was that if people changed their mindset so as to always consider the benefits of biodiversity and the costs of losing it, this would have a significant impact on the way we conduct trade.

There are now 564 biosphere reserves, including nine in Britain. These reserves combine a strictly enforced environmental protection zone with areas in which economic activity is permitted so long as it adheres to the principles of sustainable development. In 1992 the EU inaugurated a network along the same lines, entitled Natura 2000.

The more science comes to understand living organisms in all their complexity, the further the protection of nature will spread. Above all, it is biodiversity that must be preserved. Conservation efforts on their own should only serve as a reminder of what needs to change on a more fundamental level in humankind's relationship to nature. As both the human population and its impact on the planet's resources keep growing, other species will continue to disappear – and with them whole chains of interdependence that we can only guess at.

Fungal threat
Rabb's fringe-limbed tree frog, Ecnomiohyla rabborum *(below), which lives in the mountains of Panama, is critically endangered. Populations have fallen as a result of chytridiomycosis, a fungal infection of the respiratory tract.*

the services rendered by individual members of a living community and by the community as a whole. Humans self-evidently benefit from such an arrangement, with all our food, clothing and medicines deriving from Earth's great reservoir of biodiversity. It also purifies the air and water around us and regulates the climate; protection of biodiversity and human development are therefore inextricably linked. From 1971 onwards, the UN has officially acknowledged this interdependence by establishing a number of biosphere reserves.

Clinging on
The Philippine Sailfin Lizard, Hydrosaurus pustulatus *(below), is regarded as vulnerable as a result of not only being hunted for food but also being captured for sale to the pet trade.*

Robots go to war

Conflicts around the globe in the early 21st century saw the emergence of robots as a new type of combatant. Pilotless drones, unmanned ground vehicles (UGVs) and even underwater remote-operated vehicles (ROVs) are transforming the face of warfare.

Remote hunter-killer
The MQ-9 Reaper drone (above), manufactured by General Atomics, is equipped with two laser-guided bombs and four missiles. In addition to its military role, the US Homeland Security agency uses the Reaper to patrol the country's borders.

In 2001 the United States and its allies invaded Afghanistan. As they advanced, strange little tracked vehicles fitted with cameras appeared on the battlefield and on incursions into suspected insurgent hideouts. For the first time, US forces deployed robots on a large scale to undertake dangerous reconnaissance or mine-clearing missions. Remote, automated warfare had become a reality – at least on one side.

Spies in the sky

Pilotless drone aircraft came on the scene well before UGVs. In 1945, after dropping the atomic bombs on Hiroshima and Nagasaki, the US Air Force had a problem. Normally, a reconnaissance aircraft would fly over an area that had just been hit to evaluate the damage,

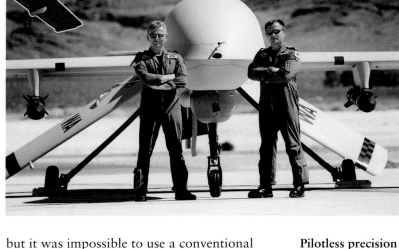

THE KETTERING BUG

The first drone with an offensive capability – the forerunner of modern cruise missile – was the US Army Signal Corps' 'Kettering Bug' of 1918. Named after its inventor, an engineer from Dayton, Ohio, it was a small biplane carrying an aerial torpedo containing 81kg of explosives, which was designed to hit targets up to 120km away. A mechanical system counted the number of engine revolutions to track the distance flown then, close to the target, cut the engine and activated a mechanism that detached the wings. The First World War ended before the plane could be used.

but it was impossible to use a conventional plane to view the effects of the atomic bombs without exposing the crew to dangerous radiation levels. From 1946 onwards, during their tests of A and H-bombs at Bikini Atoll (part of the Marshall Island chain in the South Pacific), the Americans modified obsolete B-17 'Flying Fortress' bombers to fly as remote-controlled drones through the cloud of nuclear debris and take photographs. This proved effective, but costly. In 1955 the American Radioplane Company, which had been manufacturing flying target drones for the air force for 20 years, fitted one of its planes with a camera and, more importantly, a recovery parachute. By definition, target drones were small, light craft designed to be destroyed in flight. This was the genesis of the first true drone: a pilotless aerial vehicle that could take surveillance images and return to base.

On 1 May, 1960, a high-altitude American U-2 reconnaissance plane, piloted by Lt Gary Powers, was shot down over Soviet airspace by a surface-to-air missile (SAM). This infamous

Pilotless precision
A Predator drone in Afghanistan with two of its control crew. Unmanned drones have proved highly effective against the Taliban insurgency.

incident, followed by the destruction of another U-2 during the Cuban Missile Crisis of 1962, prompted the US Air Force to promote the development of drones. With the advent of IT, pilotless drones, which are in essence simple remote-controlled devices, became true robots – autonomous and able to respond to their environment.

Yet for all their autonomy in the air, drones are just part of a much larger system: support installations on the ground include launch and recovery facilities and, above all, guidance stations for controlling and monitoring flights and gathering and analysing data. Drones make up for their lack of crew by requiring a large number of ground personnel.

Expanding deployment

The first drones to be used in the field – by the Americans in Vietnam between 1964 and 1975, and by the Israelis in Lebanon in 1982 – were basically used as decoys for anti-aircraft fire. By probing the enemy's defences, these missions collected vital information for subsequent bombing runs. Then in 1991, during the First Gulf War against Iraq, US Pioneer drones performed a different role in guiding cruise missiles down laser beams trained on targets. The successor to the Pioneer, the Predator, saw service in Bosnia (1995), Afghanistan (2001) and the Coalition invasion of Iraq in 2003.

These latter conflicts also saw the deployment of a much larger and faster type of drone than the propeller-driven Predator – the Global Hawk. This jet-engined, high-altitude, long-range craft was designed for strategic reconnaissance, radioing back in real time the data it gathered. Meanwhile, the Predator found a new role: fitted with air-to-ground

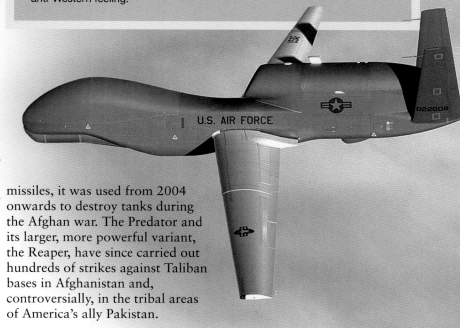

missiles, it was used from 2004 onwards to destroy tanks during the Afghan war. The Predator and its larger, more powerful variant, the Reaper, have since carried out hundreds of strikes against Taliban bases in Afghanistan and, controversially, in the tribal areas of America's ally Pakistan.

SURGICAL STRIKES?

Remote targeting by unmanned aerial vehicles raises many ethical and legal questions. Advocates of this 'surgical' mode of warfare point to the fact that drones like the Predator can 'loiter' for up to 40 hours over a target, so minimising the possibility of error. As part of the US-led 'War on Terror' in the wake of the 9/11 attacks on New York and Washington by Al Qaeda, drone bombings by the CIA have already claimed several thousand lives, chiefly in Afghanistan and Pakistan. Perhaps the most famous victim to date was Baitullah Mehsud, leader of the Pakistani Taliban, who was killed on 5 August, 2009. Wanted for his suspected involvement in the assassination of Benazir Bhutto, former prime minister of Pakistan, among other crimes, Mehsud was videoed for hours, relaxing on the flat roof of his house in the village of Zanghara in south Waziristan, by a Predator drone circling 3km above. It then launched a pair of Hellfire missiles, killing him and 11 others in the building. Yet there have been many documented cases of mistaken targeting of people who have no involvement in terrorism. As a result calls are growing for a halt to these missions, which stir up strong anti-Western feeling.

Weather watch
As well as battlefield surveillance, the US Global Hawk drone is also used by NASA to study extreme weather events. In 2010 it tracked tropical depression 'Frank' and monitored Hurricane 'Earl', which was threatening the US eastern seaboard. Missions like this would have been far too hazardous for manned aircraft.

Battlefield intelligence
The German KZO unmanned aerial vehicle is launched from the back of a lorry. The KZO is designed to detect, identify and locate enemy targets.

Targeting the Taliban
Two Reaper controllers at their base in Creech, Nevada (left). The control screen of the UAV (below), which shows the operational zone in real time, can pick out an armed man from a range of 6km.

Dawn of the UGV

Ambush early-warning
The Aladdin scouting drone, seen here (below) being launched by German soldiers in Afghanistan, is ideal for close-area imaging to look behind obstacles for enemy forces.

It is far easier for a remote-controlled vehicle to move through the air than to tackle uneven terrain on the ground. Aside from some short-range bomb-disposal robots, development of UGVs (unmanned ground vehicles) only began to get serious consideration in the 1980s; none of these early vehicles are still operational. The few UGV machines in use today are mostly small vehicles, many of them converted bomb-disposal units, but the Israeli Defence Forces have begun using a purpose-built

THE LIFESAVING BRITISH WHEELBARROW

One of the earliest UGVs was the British army's 'Wheelbarrow' robot. Devised in 1972 by Lt-Col Peter Miller, the prototype was built with parts from a wheelbarrow, hence the name, and a lawnmower. It was designed to dispose of car bombs planted by the Provisional IRA during the 'Troubles' in Northern Ireland. This small tracked vehicle had a camera, a movable arm that could smash car windows and a manipulator for opening doors and removing suspicious devices. Later versions were built with sensors that can detect chemical, biological or nuclear agents.

vehicle called the 'Guardium' on border patrol duties. In 2007 the US army sent three small experimental tracked robots armed with machine guns to Iraq, but they were never deployed in active service. Several armed forces are looking into the possibility of using UGVs in urban combat situations to flush enemy troops out of buildings.

Exploring the oceans

In the early 1960s the Americans developed the CURV ('Cable-controlled Undersea Recovery Vehicle'), a submersible with an umbilical cord – a fibre-optic cable through which images, sonar and other navigational data is tranmitted. Designed for recovering live munitions lost at sea, CURV really came into its own in 1966, when a B-52 nuclear bomber carrying four atomic weapons crashed into the Mediterranean Sea off Spain. Three of the weapons were quickly salvaged, but the fourth

AUTOMATIC DEFENCE

The European 'Goalkeeper' system is a fully automatic weapons platform that protects naval surface ships against missile attack. Mounted on deck, it comprises a turret equipped with radar that detects and locks onto incoming projectiles within six seconds, plus a rapid-fire autocannon that can deliver 5,000 rounds of heavy 30mm shells a minute. Goalkeeper and its US counterpart, the 'Phalanx' system, are known as 'close-in weapons systems' (CIWS), since they are designed to destroy sea-skimming supersonic missiles within a few hundred metres of the ship. Automated systems like these can react quicker than human gunners. The need for such protection was brought home by the sinking of the Royal Navy destroyer HMS *Sheffield*, hit by a French-made Exocet missile fired from an Argentinian aircraft during the Falklands War in 1982.

Scouting the terrain
Small UGVs like those pictured above can be carried by infantrymen and controlled from a pack no larger than a small suitcase. They are deployed in a variety of roles, from reconnaissance to mine clearance. Military equipment like this was used to probe the wreckage of the Twin Towers in New York after the 9/11 attacks.

ROV in action
The US Navy's Deep Drone submersible (right) weighs almost 2 tonnes and can dive to a depth of 2,440m, It is used on scientific expeditions and for salvage operations, such as the recovery of 'black box' flight data recorders from aircraft that have crashed at sea.

was lying some 850m down, well beyond the safe depth for divers. Within two months, the submersible had retrieved this deadly treasure. Several ROVs (remotely-operated vehicles) then followed, specially adapted for salvaging equipment, rescuing submarine crews, or mine clearance. The 1990s saw the appearance of the first crewless surface vessels, the Sea Owl and Spartan Scout, designed respectively for harbour protection duties and anti-submarine warfare. An unmanned surface vehicle built in Israel, the Protector, entered service with the Israeli armed forces and with the Republic of Singapore's navy in 2005.

A new type of war

Around the time of the First Gulf War in 1991, military strategists from the world's principal military powers, particularly the USA, began to devise an entirely new mode of strategic thinking. Registering the growing importance of satellite surveillance, stealth aircraft, 'smart' weapons systems and drones, the strategists came up with the concept of so-called 'fourth-generation warfare' (4GW). Unlike classic

Hoolicopter
This small German surveillance drone (left), resembling a mini-helicopter, has been used by police since 2008 to spot football hooligans and collect video evidence to convict them. Its compact size makes it ideal for all kinds of operations within an urban environment, including monitoring hostage situations.

DRONES IN CIVILIAN LIFE

Drones are attracting increasing interest from police forces for their stealth capabilities and cost-effectiveness – they are far less expensive to operate than a piloted helicopter. A 'Hunter' drone was sent to protect the G8 summit held at Évian in France in 2003, and to provide surveillance for the 60th anniversary celebrations of the Normandy landings in 2004; many world leaders were due to attend both events, making them a prime terrorist target. British police made their first arrest using a drone in 2010. Some forces, such as the South African police, already use drones for routine urban anti-crime surveillance. Other potential civilian uses might include monitoring traffic, shipping patrols, spotting forest fires or avalanches and border patrols (this already happens on the US-Mexico border). Many drones are currently deployed for aerial photography, such as of archaeological sites or urban regeneration projects.

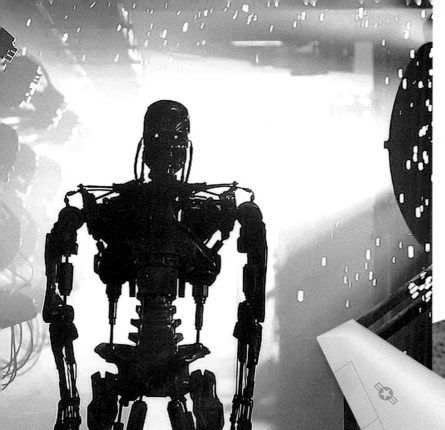

Nightmare scenario
A scene from 2009's Terminator Renaissance shows ranks of Terminators ready for action (left). Science-fiction writers and film-makers have long raised the prospect of artificially intelligent machines rising up to attack their human creators.

Ghost in the sky
The Phantom Ray UAS, unmanned airborne system (below), was unveiled by Boeing in May 2010. This new generation of spy plane will fly at 40,000ft, 10,000ft higher than commercial airliners.

conflicts of the past, this type of war is fought from a distance, in the main without deploying frontline forces except during the initial offensive. A key characteristic of 4GW is that it pits the armed forces of established states against non-state agents such as terrorist groups.

Rather than being played out in set-piece battles, this new mode of warfare places a premium on early warning and detection of threats and pre-emptive action. This, in turn, entails constant surveillance of hotspots around the globe, particularly of failed states with a power vacuum. Hence the increasing emphasis on deploying drones, satellites, extensive intelligence gathering networks and data analysis.

Ideal combatants?

Combat robots were originally developed first and foremost with an eye to minimising casualties among the armed forces and civilian populace. But with human combatants in an age of high-tech weaponry often requiring long and expensive training – pilots being a case in point – economic factors have weighed into the equation. Robots are tireless, fearless and always ready for action, outstripping the

performance of even the best soldiers in terms of speed, precision and endurance in a hostile environment. But their deployment poses serious ethical questions. International laws on conduct in war draw a clear distinction between combatants and non-combatants. At present, even on entirely automated weapons systems like drones, the decision to open fire is still taken by a human being – and even then, mistakes are made. In the future, this might not always be the case.

GEOTHERMAL ENERGY
The power of rocks

Despite being one of the first energy sources exploited by humans, geothermal energy – that is, energy from the latent heat stored in underground rocks – never really became widespread. But dwindling oil stocks have brought a resurgence of interest. Less well-known than wind or wave power, geothermal energy is not just used to heat homes, but also to generate electricity.

Natural jacuzzi
To survive the harsh winters on the Japanese island of Honshu, where temperatures can reach –15°C, macaques, Macaca fuscata (below), immerse themselves in natural hot springs, where the water is a constant 40–60°C.

The growing interest in geothermal energy – and in other renewable energy sources – from the early 2000s onwards was prompted by the increasingly urgent need to wean human society off carbon-based fossil fuels, especially coal and oil, which produce harmful greenhouse-gas emissions. Oil and natural gas are also finite resources that are rapidly running out.

The basic principle of geothermal energy is that the Earth is warm and this heat increases by an average 3.3°C for every 100m of depth

beneath the surface. The heat stems in part from the planet's core – a combination of iron and nickel that reaches 4,200°C – and from the mantle of molten rock surrounding it, whose temperature varies between 1,000 and 3,000°C. The core and mantle are not the only sources of heat within the Earth. The subsoil contains minerals such as uranium, thorium and hot potassium, whose radioactive decay accounts for 85 per cent of the heat. These sources warm subterranean water deposits, which can then be exploited as geothermal energy.

A long history

As far back as 20,000 years ago, during the last great Ice Age, it is thought that the inhabitants of the islands we now call Japan used thermal vents and geysers around volcanoes to keep warm and possibly also to cook food. This is

Natural heat
Some 40 per cent of Iceland's energy is geothermal. The 'Blue Lagoon' bathing pool (right), near the capital Reykjavik, is an artificial reservoir serving the Svartsengi geothermal power station. Far right: hot water pipes leading from the country's main geothermal facility, HS Orka.

the earliest known instance of geothermal energy use. Up to the 19th century, it was common for people to use such heat sources for similar purposes wherever they occurred. In Britain there is archaeological evidence of human activity from 8000 BC around the hot springs on which the city of Bath is built. The Romans developed these springs into *thermae*, public heated baths, just as they had in suitable locations back home. At Chaudes-Aigues in the Auvergne region of France, a network of hot springs – the hottest in Europe at 82°C – have been exploited since the Middle Ages for a variety of purposes, including washing fleeces and animal hides, heating dwellings and for health-giving spa treatments. In Italy, small natural hot basins were used as a way of obtaining sulphur from rocks.

With the dawning of the Industrial Age and its advances in mining technology, it became possible to sink boreholes to greater depths in search of geothermal energy. The result of deep drilling was even hotter water than before, often emerging in the form of steam. Thus it was that the 20th century saw the growth of two distinct types of geothermal energy: energy for heating, derived from sources 1,500–2,000m below ground and generally not exceeding 90°C; and energy for electricity generation, which tapped water sources up to 4,000m down supplying steam at temperatures of up to 150°C.

Heat for the home
The first modern urban heating network to tap into geothermal energy was established in the Icelandic capital of Reykjavik in 1930. Thereafter, other similar systems came into operation at various sites around the world. These early systems draw on hot water from around 2,000m down and either utilise direct geothermal steam ('dry steam'), or pump the water at high-pressure into lower-pressure tanks to generate so-called 'flash steam' to

Seething spring
An aerial view of Grand Prismatic Spring in Yellowstone National Park, Wyoming (above). The pool, the largest natural hot water source in the USA, is fed with water warmed by the volcanic activity beneath it.

drive turbines. Increasingly, systems today use moderately hot water from shallower geothermal reservoirs. These are called 'binary cycle power plants', since the water from underground, which is channelled into a closed circuit, transfers its warmth by means of a heat exchanger to another circuit containing a secondary fluid with a lower boiling point than water. The heat generated in this way can supply a city's hot water requirements, while also being used, say, to heat commercial greenhouses or in certain industrial processes.

A pioneering experiment

The world's first demonstration of geothermal electricity was conducted at Lardarello in southern Tuscany, Italy, in 1904. Steam emerging from geologically active ground – super-hot granite rocks lying close to the surface – turned a small turbine powering five lightbulbs. Subsequently, cold water was pumped down to enhance steam generation at temperatures of up to 220°C, and in 1911 a dry-steam power station was built at the site, first to supply electricity to the Italian railway system and later for domestic consumption. Currently around a million households are powered by geothermal electricity from

DOMESTIC GEOTHERMAL SYSTEMS

To heat individual houses, geothermal energy does not necessarily drawn on natural underground reservoirs of hot water, but instead can tap into the ambient heat present in the subsoil. These systems involve sinking vertical sensors to depths of 30–150m, or alternatively laying extensive networks of horizontal sensors, in some cases several hundred metres in length. These sensor tubes are filled with a liquid refrigerant or heat carrier), which is designed to evaporate with even the slightest rise in temperature. This fluid picks up the warmth in the soil and converts it into steam, which is sent to a heat pump where a compressor raises its temperature. A heat exchanger transfers this heat to the house's central heating system. Meanwhile the steam, condensing once more, reverts to its liquid state. These low-temperature heating systems, which run at about 50°C, distribute heat through underfloor pipes or large radiators.

A closed system
A heat pump (below), running off a geothermal probe, endlessly recycles the energy.

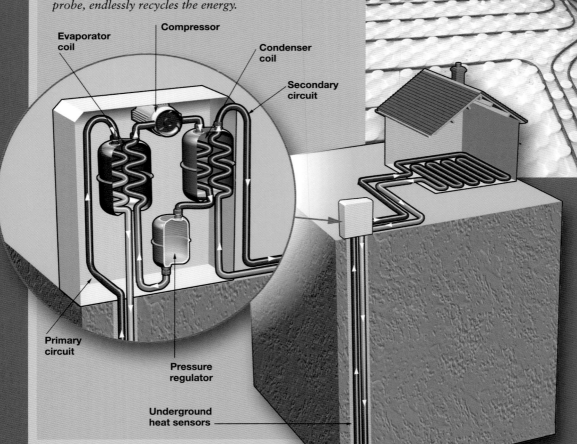

Evaporator coil

Compressor

Condenser coil

Secondary circuit

Primary circuit

Pressure regulator

Underground heat sensors

Heating in an eco-home
A heating contractor laying pipework for underfloor heating running on geothermal energy. The pipes are clipped into a heat-retaining polystyrene matrix, which is then buried under a concrete screed and flooring (tiles are best). Systems like this supply a constant flow of warm water (35–40°C) in winter, cold water (16–20°C) in summer, and can cut energy usage by up to 75 per cent compared with electric central heating.

HIGH-RISK DRILLING

Switzerland called a halt to its experimental geothermal energy programme in December 2009, after it triggered earth tremors measuring 3.4 on the Richter scale in the winter of 2006–7 near the city of Basle. The problem was caused by pumping high-pressure cold water into the ground to open up natural fissures in the rock – standard procedure in so-called 'enhanced (or engineered) geothermal systems' – thus allowing geothermal water deep down to circulate more readily. The four most violent of the 60 or so aftershocks from the Basle incident caused minor but widespread damage, mainly in the form of cracked walls. Similar seismic activity was encountered by a French team a few years earlier at Soultz-sous-Forêts. One possible way to avoid the problem is to induce the cracking more gently by chemical means. Micro-earthquakes are an inherent part of this process, but could be managed through more sophisticated drilling and constant monitoring.

Landerello – almost 5,000GWh per year, equating to 10 per cent of the world's total geothermal electricity production.

Making a comeback

Following the shock of the 1973 Oil Crisis, when Arab OPEC countries choked off the supply of oil to Western nations supporting Israel in the Yom Kippur war, several governments began looking at the potential for geothermal energy. But in typical short-term fashion, once the petrol price came down interest waned. Dwindling supplies of fossil fuels have now helped to revive the idea, especially in volcanic regions like the High Andean cordillera in South America, where geothermal fields could have massive potential for electricity generation.

Today, around 50 countries claim to be exploiting geothermal energy as a heat source. Yet production remains marginal, representing just 1 per cent of world energy consumption. Electricity generation is even less significant, with 350 power stations worldwide (202 of them in the United States) accounting for just 0.4 per cent of global needs.

The future of geothermal energy may lie in engineered deep-drilling schemes, which will penetrate beyond the reservoirs of heated water currently available and tap into ancient faultlines 5km and more below the Earth's surface. These so-called 'Enhanced Geothermal Systems' (EGS) are not without their inherent dangers, including triggering earthquakes (see box above). The largest such enterprise is a 25MW demonstration plant currently being developed in the Cooper Basin of Australia.

Magic mud
Drilling operations for geothermal energy (right) at a sustainable retail facility opened by the Japanese carmaker Toyota in La Rochelle, France, in 2010. The drilling medium is a type of mud (top), made abrasive through the addition of various minerals and aggregates. This is injected into the ground at high pressure and varying densities.

GEOTHERMAL ENERGY IN THE UK

The potential for exploiting geothermal reservoirs as a source of sustainable energy was first investigated by the Department of Energy in the wake of the 1973 Middle East oil crisis. The only scheme to come into operation was a small-scale project in Southampton, tapping water at 76°C from the Wessex basin, but teams from Newcastle and Durham universities are now drilling in various sites in the Northeast with the aim of establishing further geothermal plants. Engineers are also looking at the possibility of repurposing some North Sea drilling rigs for geothermal schemes once fossil-fuel extraction is no longer viable. A different type of plant, involving pumping water down onto geothermally heated rock, has been approved for development in 2011–13 at the Eden Project biosphere in Cornwall.

Generation Facebook

When the Friendster and MySpace sites were launched back in 2003, few people would have predicted that the number of people using social networking facilities would grow to hundreds of millions by the end of the decade. The founding of Facebook and the lawsuits that ensued became the subject of an Oscar-winning movie in 2010. As a means of fostering shared cultural or social interests, making friends online, communicating in real time or generating professional contacts, the networking phenomenon shows no signs of flagging.

Network wizards
Mark Zuckerberg (above), the CEO of Facebook, announcing new features for the site in April 2010. Above right: Evan Williams and Biz Stone, cofounders of Twitter, at their company headquarters in San Francisco.

In 2009 the number of active members on Facebook worldwide passed 400 million. In the UK alone, almost 30 million people – 58 per cent of Internet users – subscribe to this phenomenally successful site, which was created by the young American entrepreneur Mark Zuckerberg in February 2004. Facebook continues to expand and win new users among the 2 billion or so people who surf the Net. It is Zuckerberg's stated ambition to have 1 billion members on his site.

Most social networking sites are open-access, that is, they are free to join and use. Once a person has signed up, they are invited to fill in their profile by divulging various pieces of personal information, such as date of birth and e-mail address, and usually add a photo as well. The appeal of these sites is that they make people, especially teenagers, feel as though they are in the loop, and not out on a limb. They enable people to catch up with old

THINK BEFORE WRITING

In 2009 the employment-finder website CareerBuilder.com conducted a survey among 2,500 American recruiters. This found that nine out of every 20 employers in the USA visited social networking sites to check out potential job applicants before confirming an appointment. The figures broke down as follows: 29 per cent consulted Facebook, 26 per cent LinkedIn, 21 per cent MySpace, and 7 per cent Twitter. Well over half (53 per cent) of the recruiters admitted to having ruled out candidates who had posted politically extreme opinions or obscene comments, revealed that they were heavy users of drink or drugs, aired racist views, or made disparaging remarks about a previous employer. No fewer than 35 per cent of employers said that they had withdrawn job offers after looking at social networking sites. On the other hand, 18 per cent hired a candidate after being impressed by the content of his or her blog or social site page.

friends they may not have seen in years, and to make new ones, albeit most of them strictly 'virtual', living thousands of miles away.

Uses and abuses

So all-pervasive has social networking become that politicians and celebrities have caught on to Twitter and Facebook as a way of making direct contact with the general public and boosting their popularity. Companies use them to promote their image, conduct market research on their products and advertise job opportunities. They are also able to consult personal Facebook or MySpace pages to check out entries made by any prospective employees (see box, left) – the person who naïvely reveals

Calling my M8s
The explosion in smartphone ownership boosted the membership of social networking sites. Apple's iPod Touch, for instance, incorporates a Facebook app (right) that allows users to stay in constant contact with their network of friends and exchange instant messages and photos.

THE MAN WITH 400 MILLION FRIENDS

Born in 1984 in suburban New York, Mark Zuckerberg became a millionaire at the tender age of 25. One night in October 2003, in his dorm room at Harvard University, this red-headed loner hacked into the university's server and uploaded pictures of his fellow students onto a site he had created specially, called Facemash. Visitors to the site were invited to link the picture of their chosen 'victim' to images of farm animals. Zuckerberg incurred the wrath of the college authorities, but persisted. Ultimately, with their blessing, he created a legitimate social networking site, Thefacebook.com. Originally limited to Harvard students, the site was soon thrown open to other Ivy League universities such as Stanford, Yale and Columbia. Facebook became an open-access site to all in 2006 and has enjoyed meteoric success ever since.

all their youthful indiscretions, often with photographs, may come to regret it. All an inquisitive human resources manager needs to do is follow these indelible digital fingerprints on a search engine like Google.

There are other, more sinister sides to social networking. Hackers use these sites as a portal through which to bombard people with spam, viruses and malware, perhaps to gain access to personal financial details and other sensitive data. And there have been many recorded cases of paedophiles 'grooming' vulnerable children through Facebook or MySpace by pretending to be friends of the same age, before luring their target into a face-to-face meeting.

EPIGENETICS – 2003
DNA is not destiny

The reason why identical twins develop differently and why, for example, only one of them becomes prone to diseases like asthma, is that genes are not unchanging keys to the way we all turn out. In the early 21st century confirmation of the fact that the genome is not an unvarying code turned genetics and the other life sciences on their heads.

Moulded by history
The enduring effects of hardship suffered by those who lived through the Second World War have in some cases been passed on to future generations. Studies of obesity resistance in the Netherlands found that even children born after the war ended could not put on excessive weight. This queue for food (left) was in occupied France.

Ever since Francis Crick and James Watson, using groundbreaking X-ray data produced by Rosalind Franklin, discovered the double helix structure of DNA, the theory of innate and acquired characteristics passed down through genetic inheritance reigned supreme. According to this theory, genes formed the innate element up to a person's birth, while the resulting individual was then modified by acquired traits, rather like a musician interpreting a score. All challenges to this orthodoxy were decried as 'Lamarckism', referring to the French biologist Jean-Baptiste Lamarck (1744-1829), whose theory of inheritance maintained that an organism can pass on to its offspring characteristics acquired during its lifetime.

But a number of awkward facts appeared to refute the established view. Doctors and medical researchers in the Netherlands were

SUPPORTING EVOLUTION

Far from undermining Charles Darwin's theory of evolution, the discovery of the epigenome has served to corroborate it. It confirmed that the structure of DNA is unchanging, so that a rabbit, for example, cannot give birth to a mouse, but what it altered was our understanding of how quickly species can evolve. In the 19th century Darwin and his followers believed that this took place over extremely long periods – tens or hundreds of thousands of years – and could only occur through mutation. Now, in certain cases, it is possible to see evolution as a more rapid process, particularly in an environment that fosters the activity of markers. This suggests a key to human heredity, explaining why, for example, genius seems to be a heritable trait in certain families, such as that of the composer Johann Sebastian Bach.

Passing patterns on
Segments of DNA from a mother (left) and her offspring (right). Genes activated by repressor genes and effector genes are shown in red and green respectively. Activated or suppressed during the parent's life by factors such as diet, illness or stress, some of them reappear in the child's genetic make-up. The reasons for this selection still await a scientific explanation.

astonished to find that the children and even grandchildren of women who had survived the hardships of the Second World War appeared to have an inbuilt resistance to becoming obese, despite the fact that food had long since become plentiful and people were well-nourished. Research conducted in the 1980s by Swedish specialist Lars Olov Bygren made a decisive contribution to our understanding of this phenomenon.

Lamarck vindicated

Since 1986 it has been known that children whose mothers had a disruption in their diet during pregnancy run a greater risk of developing cardiovascular diseases. At first, this was thought to be the result of traumas suffered by the foetus during development, with genetics playing no part. But Bygren's work, which extended to grandchildren, suggested that acquired characteristics can become hereditary.

At the instigation of theoretical geneticists, such as Britain's Marcus Pembrey, researchers set about investigating this enigma. Twenty years later, the concept of epigenetics began to take shape. The term, formed from the Greek root *epi-*, meaning 'above', describes a biological mechanism through which 'markers' attach to certain genes. These can either block these genes or alternatively stimulate them to express themselves if they are dormant. These markers (methyl groups) do not alter the structure of the DNA but rather the modes of gene expression. They are produced by the organism in response to certain conditions, such as overconsumption of food or alcohol, drug addiction or stress – and are hereditary.

Final proof of epigenesis was provided in 2003 by cancer specialist Randy L Jirtle and his assistant Robert A Waterland at Duke University in North Carolina. After genetically modifying pregnant mice by making them express what they called the 'agouti gene' (which predisposed the mice to obesity and diabetes, and turned their coats yellow), they separated them into two groups. One group was fed with a diet rich in vitamin B, while the other was given normal food. When the mice gave birth, the infants born to the special-diet group were yellow, while the others were brown and healthy, as normal. The B vitamins acted as markers, releasing the expression of the agouti gene through methylation. This showed beyond doubt that the epigenome is hereditary.

A DISTURBING STUDY

In the 1980s Lars Olov Bygren, a specialist in preventative hygiene from the Karolinska Institute in Stockholm, was alarmed to discover that the inhabitants of the small Swedish town of Överkalix had lower than normal life expectancy and displayed abnormally high incidence of cardiovascular events such as heart attacks and strokes. Choosing 99 people at random in the town from those born in 1905, he began a painstaking investigation into their environment and lifestyle over three generations. He concluded that the children and grandchildren of those who had eaten to excess were prone to cardiovascular disease, even though they themselves were not overeaters. The difference he found was huge, reducing their life expectancy by 32 years on average.

Amazing variety
All dogs descend from two common ancestors, the grey wolf (Canis lupus) *and the jackal* (Canis aureus), *from more than 12 million years ago. Since then they have diversified into hundreds of breeds of different shapes and sizes.*

Inheriting unhealthiness
Following the discovery of epigenesis, epidemiologists now act on the awareness that obesity may be a heritable affliction.

EPIGENETIC MEDICINES

The first epigenetic drug went on sale in 2004: Azacitide prolongs the life of those affected by a rare blood disorder. Several others are at development stage.

BIOFUELS
The green gold rush

Fuels produced from plants, a renewable resource, were developed at the turn of the 21st century in response to the depletion of petroleum reserves and the need to cut harmful greenhouse gas emissions. Yet the ecological benefits of biofuels appear far less impressive than once claimed, and they divert valuable land away from growing crops for food.

On a global scale, the production of biofuels tripled between 2000 and 2007, by which time it represented 2 per cent of all fuel used. The first venture into this new field was ethanol, an alcohol produced by fermenting either sugar beet or sugar cane, the main method, or alternatively cereal starch obtained from wheat or maize. The ethanol was then transformed into EthylTertioButylEther (ETBE) through reaction with isobutene, a by-product of the oil refining process. Brazil and the United States alone account for 77 per cent of world demand for ethanol; in 2007 Brazil turned over 54 per cent of its cane sugar production to biofuels, while 23 per cent of US maize was earmarked for this purpose.

Following on from ethanol came biodiesel, obtained through a chemical reaction between a vegetable oil – for example, sunflower, rapeseed, soya or palm oil – and methanol.

The European Union supplies 63 per cent of the world's biodiesel, and devoted 47 per cent of its vegetable oil production to the product in 2008.

Future generations

Researchers seeking substitutes for fossil fuels continue to spread their net ever wider. So-called 'second-generation' biofuels include extracts from wood shavings, straw and specially cultivated woody plants. Fibrous materials can be transformed, through gasification and then chemical synthesis, into biodiesel. Or they can be subjected to enzymatic hydrolysis – a process of decomposition through the action of water in the presence of digesting enzymes – followed by fermentation to produce ethanol. But there are technological obstacles to applying this treatment on an industrial scale.

Green gasoline?
Bioethanol E85 fuel (above) contains a mixture of 85 per cent bioethanol with 15 per cent unleaded petrol. Car engines need to be adapted to run on this fuel, which produces fewer harmful emissions than petrol.

Another approach is to manufacture ethanol using oil-bearing non-food plants, such as *Jatropha curcas* or *Pongamia pinnata*. From the spurge and pea families respectively, these crops are already being grown from India to Mozambique. They have the advantage of being drought-resistant and are able to flourish in regions unsuitable for the cultivation of traditional crops. A third generation of biofuels, involving the cultivation of micro-algae, is at the trial phase; the yields are anticipated to be some 30 to 100 times greater than those of land-grown oil-bearing plants.

Pressure on resources

After an initial phase of euphoria surrounding biofuels – or 'agrofuels' as some people prefer to call them – independent studies have since taken much of the shine off their image. In 2008 the UN's Food and Agriculture Organization (FAO) released a highly critical report highlighting the role biofuel crops played in the dramatic rise in global food prices since 2006. Projections indicate that it will be impossible to feed the expanding human population while continuing to turn more and more land over to agrofuels.

New generations of fuels may provide a solution to this dilemma – in theory, at least. In practice, in both Mozambique and India, the cultivation of *Jatropha* has progressively squeezed out food-producing crops. And in Brazil, the huge expansion in industrial sugar cane plantations has driven subsistence farmers off their smallholdings, is steadily encroaching on the Amazonian rainforest, and is now

BRAZIL'S FUEL REVOLUTION

Starting in 1975, Brazil's government launched a national programme to produce ethanol from cane sugar. It saw rapid initial growth, temporarily declined when petrol prices fell in 1986, then production soared from the early 2000s onwards. By 2006 seven out of every 10 new vehicles sold in Brazil were 'Flexible Fuel Vehicles' running on biofuel. Ethanol accounted for 40 per cent of the country's total fuel consumption and, for the first time in its history, Brazil's energy exports matched its imports. In the long term, demand threatens to outstrip supply, so Brazil's agriculture ministry reduced the legal minimum proportion of ethanol added to fuels from 25 to 20 per cent.

Crops for biofuel
Above, left to right: oil palms in Borneo; a wheatfield in the Netherlands; and sugar canes being cut in Brazil. The financial lure of biofuel cultivation is leading some countries to turn an increasing acreage over to such crops, with a detrimental impact on the natural environment.

Friendly fuel?
The fact that seeds from the Barbados nut plant Jatropha curcas *(right) are not edible made them a candidate for growing as a biofuel crop in developing countries. It was thought they would not compete with food crops, but they still take land away from food cultivation .*

beginning to threaten other areas of uniquely rich biodiversity such as the Pantanal. Similarly, the tropical forest of southern Asian and its inhabitants are fast retreating in the face of commercial oil-palm plantations, the cheapest

Unpopular practices
Not only do biofuels stand accused of promoting the development of monocultures that destroy biodiversity, but much of the maize and soya grown for biofuel purposes are GM crops.

NOTHING NEW

The 4-stroke engine developed by Nikolaus Otto, co-founder of BMW, ran on ethanol, as did the engine of the famous Model-T Ford, the world's first mass-produced car. And Rudolf Diesel's internal combustion engine was designed to run happily on vegetable oil.

ETHANOL ENGINE COMPATIBILITY

When used in biofuels, ethanol is mixed with petroleum in varying proportions, from just 5 per cent in Europe to a maximum of 25 per cent in Brazil. Within the EU it is most often incorporated in the form of ETBE to improve the octane rating (a measure of its detonation resistance, or 'anti-knocking' capacity) of unleaded petrol. Petrol engines can run on a blend of 5 per cent bioethanol (E5) without any modifications, but cars with flexi-fuel (or dual fuel) equipment installed can use blends of up to 85 per cent, that is, with just 15 per cent traditional petrol. The same applies to biodiesel: blends of less than 20 per cent biodiesel can be used in diesel engines with no, or minor modifications. Most European vehicles use a 5 per cent biodiesel-to-diesel mix (B5). Diesel engines can even run on pure vegetable oil, although this greatly increases the risk of them clogging up.

source of biodiesel starter. The mounting pressure on natural resources is also evident from figures published by UNESCO in 2009: every litre of biofuel manufactured requires between 1,000 and 4,000 litres of water.

A false dawn?

It remains to be seen whether the contribution made by biofuels to energy saving and to the fight against global warming can really offset their direct social and environmental costs. The evidence is inconclusive, with figures varying wildly according to the source, the calculation method and the particular fuels in question. The 'energy balance' – that is, the ratio of the amount of energy released by a fuel divided by the amount of energy used in making it (sometimes called the 'net energy gain') – fluctuates from an impressive 8 to 10 for sugar cane ethanol to a negative figure of 0.93 for ETBE. However, the energy balance of Brazilian sugar-cane ethanol falls dramatically to 5 if measured on its arrival at the port of Rotterdam, factoring in the fuel expended in shipping it, and the efficiency quotient of all these biofuels diminishes when the loss of traditional by-products such as animal feed is taken into account.

A similar story emerges concerning the emission of greenhouse gases. At face value,

MICROALGAE AS FUEL

The first decade of the 21st century saw a proliferation of research in such far-flung places as the Gulf coast of Texas, the Negev Desert in Israel and China into the cultivation of microalgae for fuel. Many of these single-celled organisms, or diatoms, are rich in oils which are being use to make experimental aviation fuels. They are grown in huge saltwater basins and thrive on strong concentrations of carbon dioxide, so cultivation plants could potentially be set up alongside thermal power stations or cement works as a way of absorbing harmful emissions. On the other hand, they require large amounts of fertiliser, plus other chemicals to prevent other micro-organisms from multiplying. According to one of the firms leading this research, a tract of land equivalent to the size of Maryland, which is a little over 32,000km^2, turned over to microalgae cultivation would meet the USA's total fuel requirements.

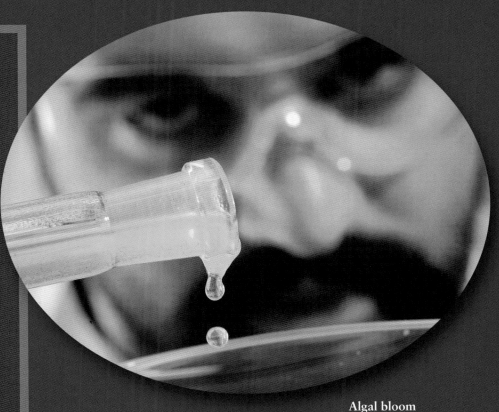

according to the most favourable statistics, burning 1 litre of biodiesel or ethanol produces four times less carbon dioxide than burning 1 litre of petrol or diesel. Yet this figure becomes far less impressive when all the emissions associated with growing the crops and producing and delivering the fuel are factored in – factors such as manufacturing fertilisers, running farm machinery, crop irrigation and transportation of the end product over long distances. When this is done, wheat ethanol, maize-based biodiesel and palm-oil biodiesel are all shown to have a larger carbon footprint than diesel.

Clearly, a more sober appraisal of biofuels is called for. At best, they provide an interim solution to the fossil fuel problem while the world waits for alternative means of propulsion, such as fuel cells, to become feasible. At worst, the false dawn they offer is impeding the development of essential new models of economic and energy policy.

Algal bloom
A scientist (above) examining a sample of Chlorella vulgaris, *a genus of single-celled algae currently being used to develop third-generation biofuels. The yield of one hectare of these microalgae could be as much as 30 times that of maize.*

Fuel cycle
A tank for cultivating the Chlorella vulgaris *algae (left). The cultivation plant uses waste from the process to generate methane, which is burned to generate electricity, while the resulting carbon dioxide is pumped back into the tanks to promote the growth of the algal bloom.*

Far more than just a phone

The rise of the Internet was the impetus behind the development of the smartphone. In 2004 the Universal Mobile Telecommunications System (UMTS) was rolled out across Europe, marking the birth of the third generation (3G for short) of mobile phone networks. Cellphones were no longer just for calling people; they had morphed into portable multimedia platforms.

During the 1990s the World Wide Web came on in leaps and bounds, creating what people soon came to refer to as the 'virtual' world. Mobiles phones had to keep pace with these advances, but second-generation cellphone networks, their communications protocols and the handsets themselves were not designed to cope with multimedia data transmissions.

The communications protocol to meet these needs evolved quite naturally from the development of the Web – the TCP/IP Internet protocol suite. UMTS, the first true third-generation telephone technology, was trialled in 2002 in Austria and Norway before being made generally available across Europe in 2004, offering a download speed of up to 1.9 megabits/sec (in practice, several hundred kB/s). All this upgrading cost mobile phone operators dear: it was not possible to adapt their existing GSM, the Global System for Mobile Communications, so they had to create a new network from scratch.

Swift progress
The Nokia 'Communicator' phone launched in 1996 (above) represented the 'Stone Age' of smartphone technology: it weighed 400g, was 4cm thick, and flipped open to reveal the user interface of a black-and-white screen and QWERTY keyboard. By comparison, Motorola's state-of-the-art Flipout of 2010 (right) weighs in at 120g and is slim enough to fit in a pocket.

From the Communicator to the iPhone

The revolution in handsets dates from Nokia's 'Communicator' phone of 1996, which could not only send and receive texts but also offered (limited) Internet connectivity. Before long, the Canadian BlackBerry was approaching development from the opposite angle, by adding a mobile phone to an electronic organiser. Convergence towards a universal multimedia device was clearly underway.

Smartphones combine advanced telephony functions – voice transmission, text messaging, music downloads, the sending and receiving of photos – with more professional applications such as work schedules, e-mail, Net access and

smartphones and 3g phones

a dictaphone. Equipped with operating systems and the ability to add new applications ('apps'), Nokia smartphones (from 1996 onwards), the BlackBerry (1999) and later the Apple iPhone (2007) became true pocket computers; apps include e-mail and word-processing software, spreadsheets, games and much more besides. This area has seen the fiercest competition between rival manufacturers and, just as it did in the world of desktop and traditional computers, Linux software is trying to capture market share from more established players.

Smartphone uses

When mobile phone operators put in bids for 3G licenses (a hugely expensive business – in the UK alone, the Treasury netted £23 million from the auction in 2000), they banked on their networks being used mainly for pay television and videophone access. In the event, these features were technological dead-ends. The real boom area for smartphones was the explosion of social networking sites on the Web. Users – especially teenagers and young adults, the aficionados of the technology – use their phones primarily to stay in touch with friends, but smartphones have also supplanted MP3 players for music downloads. Business professionals traded in electronic personal organisers for smartphones. With greater bandwidth availability and the spread of mobile technology, smartphones have been adopted by the general public of all ages to fulfil a wide variety of uses once reserved for computers with Internet access, from research to online shopping.

With bandwidth availability becoming ever more pressing, some operators are anticipating jumping directly from second to fourth generation networks: 4G systems such as WiMAX or LTE were at the test stage in 2010. As smartphones grow ever more sophisticated and as new apps are introduced on an almost daily basis, the demand for these indispensable aids to modern living seems likely to continue to soar in the coming years.

Fruitful developments
The BlackBerry (top right) found a ready market among business travellers; its revolutionary Push Mail function alerted users in real time to the arrival of new messages in the Inbox. Apple's iPhone (above) brought touchscreen technology to the mobile phone. The AppStore, a virtual shop with thousands of applications, was launched especially to support the device.

INSTANT WITNESS

Camcorders were first incorporated into mobile phones in 2006. Manufacturers originally envisaged callers using them when phoning, but their most popular application has been for capturing live events. As events unfold on the street, anyone with a smartphone can record them. The impact is all the greater as the images can instantly be uploaded, with no filter or censorship, to the Web and broadcast on video-sharing sites like YouTube. Increasingly, protesters are using this method to document human-rights abuses during anti-government protests in repressive regimes.

Capturing the moment
A 'flashmob' caught by smartphone. This dance event in Berlin in August 2009 was part of a global tribute to Michael Jackson.

NEW RESEARCH INTO BRAIN FUNCTIONS
Delving deep into the mind

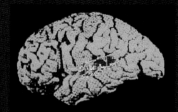

The turn of the 21st century heralded a new era in brain research. State-of-the-art techniques like functional MRI (fMRI) scanning and molecular biology have revealed the extraordinary adaptability of this vital organ and the amazing complexity of its functions, opening a whole new chapter in the history of neurology.

The brain in action
Medical imaging techniques have contributed enormously to advances in our understanding of brain physiology. Positron Emission Tomography (PET) has produced scans that show the areas of the human brain that are involved in different functions. The two PET scans (top left) highlight in red and yellow the areas of the brain that are active during word recognition and repetition. These parts of the brain are involved when music students like these (left) sing or play instruments.

On 17 July 1990, President George Bush announced the beginning of the 'Decade of the Brain' in the United States. A similar initiative followed in Europe and subsequently spread around the world. The fruits of the various research efforts that resulted became clear in the final years of the 20th century, with great advances in the field of neurology.

Synaptic plasticity

First and foremost, the view of the brain as a static unchanging organ was exploded once and for all. Studies in the 1990s revealed that the architecture of the brain can be highly flexible. This corroborated the work of the pioneering Canadian neuroscientist Donald Hebb, who introduced his theory of 'synaptic plasticity' in 1949. Hebb argued that the brain reconfigures its neural pathways as experience dictates, with the efficacy of the synapses (the areas of contact between nerve cells) varying according to whether they form part of a well-used network or not.

The stimulations the brain is subjected to during childhood gradually facilitate the formation and consolidation of neuronal circuits, which play a key role in sensorimotor control, memory, creativity and cognitive abilities. From the first months in a person's life, the proliferation of synaptic connections begins in the visual cortex and continues up to puberty in the frontal lobes, the centre of emotional control and personality. Provided all the essential structures have formed by adulthood, synaptic plasticity allows for a degree of 'fine tuning'.

Another major discovery was the vital role played in this process by astrocytes – star-shaped glial cells that provide physical and nutritional support for neurons. From the late 1990s onwards, a team led by Ben Barres at Stanford University, California, showed that astrocytes secrete chemical factors which stimulate the formation of new synapses. As well as communicating with one another, the cells are also able to amplify or interrupt nerve impulses. Astrocytes are therefore fundamental to memory and learning.

Constant renewal
Another long-cherished notion that new research has disproved is that of human babies being born with a stockpile of some 100 billion neurons that dwindle throughout an individual's life. From 1992 on, a group of Canadian researchers investigated stem cells in the brains of adult mice, which could be cultured to propagate a range of new neurons. In 1996 Elizabeth Gould from the University of Princeton in New Jersey, reported having observed the formation of new neurons in two areas of the brain in adult monkeys – the hippocampus and the olfactory bulbs. Two years later, Peter Eriksson of the University of Gothenburg in Sweden and

Nerve cell growth
A fluorescent light micrograph of cells following stimulation by nerve growth factor (below). The cell bodies contain the nuclei (pink). The spherical cells have formed long branching extensions called neurites (yellow and blue). These neurites proceed to form the axons and dendrons that connect nerve cells and transmit nerve impulses around the body, the brain and spinal cord.

MIRROR NEURONS
In 1995, Italian neuroscientist Giacomo Rizzolatti was sharing a pizza with colleagues at the University of Parma when he noticed something remarkable about one of the macaque monkeys in his lab, which had electrodes attached to its brain. The animal's motor cortex showed the same activity, as if it had also been reaching for a slice of pizza, although it had not moved at all. Brain imaging later revealed the presence of such 'mirror neurons' in humans, responding to stimuli in people watching actions just as they did in those doing them. These neurons condition our ability to empathise.

Man versus monkey
Neurology seems set to show whether humans share mental faculties with other primates. In this, it is going a step further than ethology, which is limited to studying animal behaviour.

HOW WE REMEMBER

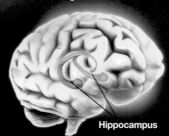

3 CONSOLIDATION
Information will be lost if it is not consolidated. This is a continuous and very slow process. The hippocampus plays a central role since it is this that distributes information related to the memory in the neocortex.

Cingulate gyrus

Anterior thalamus

Mamillary body

Hippocampus

Right frontal lobe

Mamillary body

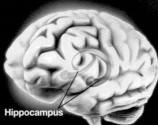

Left frontal cortex

Hippocampus

1 ENCODING
Each new piece of information comes to the brain via the senses. The brain encodes it and converts it into a mnesic (memory) trace for storage.

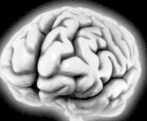

2 STORAGE (OR RETENTION)
The coded information is permanently stored in the neocortex, which occupies the uppermost levels of the cerebral hemispheres (blue areas): the occipital lobe for detailed visual information and the external temporal lobe for verbal data.

Right frontal lobe

4 RETRIEVAL
(also called restitution or recall) The better coded a memory is, the easier it is to retrieve. When the memory is recalled automatically, it is the hippocampus that is activated, while the right frontal cortex comes into play during a conscious effort to remember a fact.

Hippocampus

Intelligence dissected

Medical imaging techniques have revealed the various localised functions of the brain such as memory. For instance, we know that coding of information takes place in the left frontal lobe and the hippocampus, while storage occurs in the neocortex. Memory consolidation – our ability to fix facts long-term – takes place in the hippocampus and anterior thalamus, while retrieval is in the hippocampus and the right frontal lobe.

'DOING THE KNOWLEDGE'

Taxi drivers in most cities only need a driving licence, but to be a London cabbie applicants must learn 320 routes then take a special test. To prepare, they ride around the capital on mopeds 'doing the knowledge'. A study in 2000 found that the hippocampus of London cabbies was larger than that of control subjects, and that it grew with experience.

Fred Gage of the Salk Institute in California revealed that the adult human hippocampus generates large numbers of neurons. The researchers conceived the idea of examining the brain tissue of patients who had died of cancer, but who, as part of their treatment, had been injected with a radioactive substance to monitor the growth of malignant cells. The presence of this substance in neurons situated within the hippocampus – a brain area key to spatial memory – clearly indicated that these had only developed after the injection.

In 2003 a team from the Pasteur Institute in Paris led by Pierre-Marie Lledo discovered another site of neurogenesis, or neuron creation, behind the olfactory bulb. After an injury, the brain appears to have regenerative powers, even among elderly subjects.

Brain imaging

All these discoveries owe a great deal to multiphoton microscopy, a technique based on fluorescence imaging introduced in 1996. In general, advances made in imaging techniques, allied with those in computing and sensors, have provided researchers with an amazing new battery of tools for examining brain function. The First International Conference on Functional Mapping of the Human Brain was held in Paris in 1995.

Functional imaging, which provides images of the brain in action, is now a well-established area of research. Its two principal techniques, positron emission tomography (PET) and functional magnetic resonance imaging (fMRI), produce high-resolution images in real time and have enabled researchers to refine the cartography of the brain. In the 2000s diffusion MRI – another promising technique that makes it possible to see infinitesimally small movements of water molecules – began providing images of even higher resolution.

The era of cognitive neurosciences may truly be said to have arrived. In this field, the Portuguese-American researcher Antonio Damasio has highlighted certain zones of the cerebral cortex activated by facial recognition, as well as neuronal sites involved in emotional states, notably at the level of the prefrontal cortex. In Britain, teams such as those at the centre for Neuroscience in Education at Cambridge University are investigating the cerebral structures engaged by learning to read, do arithmetic and make music.

Determinants of behaviour

Medical imaging, neurophysiology and neurochemistry have combined to reveal the mechanisms that come into play in human behaviour. Scientists have discovered new neurotransmitters – substances released at the level of the synapses which transmit nerve signals from one neuron to another. In 1998, for example, orexin, which is believed to play a part in regulating both sleep and appetite, was identified in the hypothalamus by Dr Takeshi Sa... at the University of Tsukuba in Japan and by Dr Luis de Lecca at Stanford.

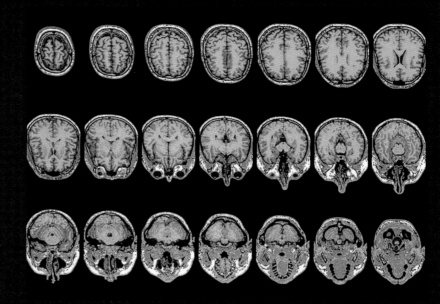

Slice by slice
Twenty-one coloured images produced by MRI scanning show sections through a healthy human brain, beginning (top left) at the top of the cerebral hemispheres and proceeding to the base of the skull (bottom right). In the lower scans, the nasal cavity and the jaw can be seen.

THE SLEEP GENE

Californian researchers have found that the varying amounts of sleep different people need is genetically pre-programmed. In 2009 they demonstrated that a mutation of the DEC2 gene, which is involved in regulating biorhythms, in a mother and daughter led to them both requiring far less sleep than average.

Healthy appetite
The urge to eat is an essential life function, but it needs to be regulated. This role is performed by leptin, a protein produced by white fat cells in adipose tissue, which acts on receptors in the hypothalamus of the brain. Below: a computer-generated model of a leptin molecule.

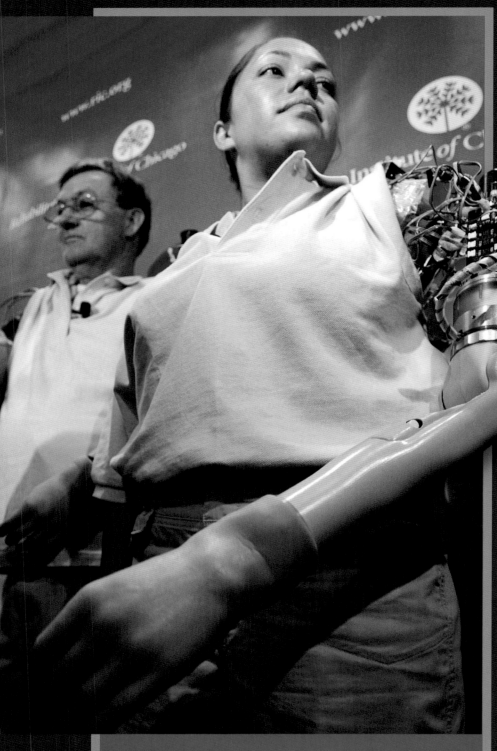

A whole range of different neuroreceptors were identified around the same time. Present on the surface of neurons, these capture not only neurotransmitters but also hormones and psychotropic substances, such as drugs and medication, carried by the bloodstream. Digestive behaviour can also involve complex actions by a number of active hormones on the hypothalamus, particularly leptin, a protein hormone produced by fat cells which was discovered in 1994, and ghrelin, an appetite-stimulating hormone secreted in the stomach lining, first identified in 1999. In 1996, US researcher Chris Saper pinpointed neurons close to the optic chiasm that are active during sleep but inactive during wakefulness, due to the brain releasing an inhibitory neurotransmitter.

Research into the biological basis of addiction has also seen some important advances. The function of the reward system – an agglomeration of brain structures that regulates and controls behaviour and so has a major bearing on dependence – was analysed around the turn of the 21st century. Scientists such as Gaetano Di Chiara in Italy and Wolfram Schultz in Switzerland have highlighted the strategic role played by activation of the neurotransmitter dopamine in the 'nucleus accumbens', a collection of neurons located in the very centre of the forebrain (striatum).

Alleviating brain disorders

Neurobiology is finding common ground with other disciplines, such as neuroendocrinology, which studies the interactions between the central nervous system and the endocrine (hormonal) system, and psycho-neuro-immunology, which investigates the permanent interaction between the brain and the immune system. The harmful effects of stress on the brain, for example, are related to increased levels of cortisol, a stress hormone produced by the adrenal glands. The links between stress, depression and anomalies in cortisol production have been the subject of studies by many researchers, notably the American Rachel Yehuda in work on post-traumatic stress disorder. High cortisol levels are harmful to the hippocampus, and have negative impacts on memory and concentration. They can also influence a person's mood by altering the secretion of neurotransmitters. Other studies have made a connection between stress, depression and immune deficiencies.

A number of studies underline the impact of nutritional factors and hygiene on the brain. A diet rich in folic acid and Omega-3 fatty

BIONIC WOMAN

In 2006 ex-US marine Claudia Mitchell became the first woman to receive a 'bionic' limb at the Rehabilitation Institute of Chicago. Mitchell, who lost her left arm in a motorbike accident, was fitted with a prosthetic limb that could detect messages from the brain via electrodes attached to her chest. There, shoulder nerves that once ran to the amputated arm had been grafted onto pectoral muscles in a procedure called 'muscle re-innervation'. This enabled her to grasp objects or turn the pages of a book just by thinking about it.

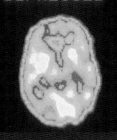

NORMAL

DEPRESSED

Revealing mental states
When combined with neurochemistry, medical imaging can explain hitherto unfathomable mental states: for instance, a PET-scan analysis of deoxyglucose levels can clearly distinguish a clinically depressed patient (left).

acids has been shown to foster brain development. Antioxidants such as fruit polyphenols, tea and wine have beneficial effects on neuronal signalling and behaviour, helping to protect the brain against the ageing process and neurodegenerative diseases. In the context of an increasingly ageing population, this is an important line of research.

The first active medication to replace acetylcholine neurons, which are depleted by Alzheimer's Disease, appeared in the United States in 1993. Administered early, it can slow the onset of the illness, but prescription is limited by the fact that the drug has a toxic effect on the liver, the key organ for metabolising most medication. A less toxic second generation of this same class of drug (cholinesterase inhibitors) came on the market with the launch of Donepezil (Aricept) in 1997. Another form of treatment, which acts on disturbances affecting glutamate neurons (one of the six known neurotransmitters) followed in 2002.

There have been some significant breakthroughs in the treatment of Parkinson's Disease. From 1993 a French team under Dr Marc Peschanski began experimenting with the procedure of foetal neuron grafts – the first full clinical trial took place three years later on a patient suffering from Huntington's Disease, a hereditary neurodegenerative illness. And beginning in 1995 tests were conducted using Deep Brain Stimulation (DBS) to try to reduce the motor symptoms of Parkinson's, with some positive results.

THE BRAIN'S AGEING GENE

In 2009 Gilbert Bernier of the University of Montreal in Canada discovered a mutation in mice that dramatically accelerated the ageing process in the cerebral cortex. The gene in question was Bmi1, which in its normal state regulates the ageing of neurons in the central nervous system by preventing the build-up of toxic free radicals.

Early warning
Magnetoencephalography (MEG) measures the magnetic fields created by neuron activity. It is used to detect signs of incipient epilepsy and Alzheimer's Disease, as well as psychiatric and cognitive function disorders.

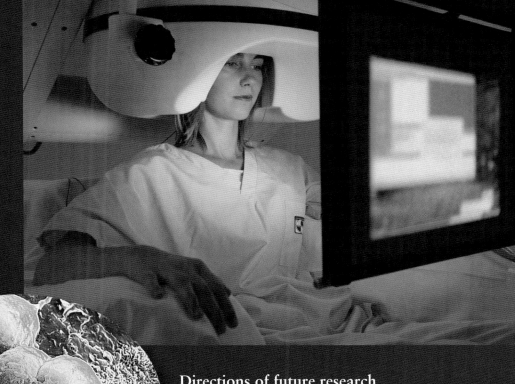

Directions of future research

Although the initial results of foetal neuron grafts have been encouraging, improvements in patients' brain function still needs to be corroborated on a larger scale. New strategies are currently being explored, such as developing a therapeutic vaccine against Alzheimer's and gene therapy or stem-cell treatment to combat Parkinson's.

Another important strand in current brain research focuses on the link between genetics and mental illness. The genetic trajectory is being examined across a whole range of disorders, from schizophrenia to manic depression. One key breakthrough in this field was the discovery of a gene associated with autism in 2003. In a totally different area, researchers are studying the possibility of artificially enhancing impaired hearing and sight through direct brain stimulation, and investigating the interface between the brain and machines.

New brain material
Neuronal grafts are as straightforward and viable as other grafting procedures. This electron microscope image (above) shows a cluster of recently grafted foetal neurons .

Gazing deep into the universe

Barring some technological miracle, rockets will never enable humans to reach anything but the nearest stars. So to observe the cosmos in close detail, astronomers have no other choice than to create ever more powerful telescopes. Very large array telescopes have been remarkably successful in probing the deepest reaches of space.

As the sun sets over Chile's Atacama Desert, the mountain known as Cerro Paranal comes to life. Here, situated at an altitude of 2,550m, are four giant telescopes, each equipped with an 8.2m diameter reflector, which as darkness falls slowly turn to face the first stars that appear. Alongside are four smaller telescopes in domed housings, each with a 1.8m reflector. Together, they make up the VLTI (Very Large Telescope Interferometer), the most powerful such instrument in the world. They were installed between 2004 and 2008, and the facility is operated by the European Southern Observatory (ESO). The telescopes are interconnected to form a single supertelescope with a reflector the equivalent of 200m in diameter. This means that the VLTI is able to magnify the stars it observes 30,000 times, far outstripping the capacity of the most famous telescope to date, the Hubble Space Telescope (HST). In orbit around the Earth since 1990, the HST has a magnification of x1,200.

Seeing further and further

The VLTI is the latest leader in a long-running contest to build ever-larger telescopes. The race began in the late 18th century, when the German-born British composer and amateur astronomer William Herschel discovered the planet Uranus through a telescope with a 23cm diameter mirror. In 1789, in Slough, he and his mathematician sister Caroline constructed their famous '40-foot Telescope' (referring to its focal length) which had a 1.2m primary mirror. Using this, they were the first to observe binary stars. In 1800 Herschel made a key discovery for the future of astronomy by proving the existence of infrared radiation, a phenomenon hitherto invisible to the human eye. Infrared was just one part of the light spectrum, which was gradually revealed over the course of the 19th and 20th centuries, with the discovery first of ultraviolet light, then X-rays, gamma rays, and so on.

First of the giants
The Mount Wilson Solar Observatory under construction in California in 1916 (far left). The observatory houses two telescopes, one of which – the Hooker, seen below in 1995 – was the first to be equipped with an interferometer. The telescope was taken out of commission in 1986, but restarted in 1992 after being outfitted with adaptive optics.

The class of very indistinct and hazy stars known as nebulae prompted astronomers to build even more powerful telescopes. Nebulae had been the subject of speculation since their discovery in the 18th century. Some observers claimed they were turbulent clouds of gas, while others maintained that they were

GRAVITATIONAL LENSES

In 2001 the Hubble Space Telescope observed stars situated 13 billion light years from Earth. This astonishing distance brought researchers close to the limits of the known universe, and its origin in the singularity called the Big Bang. To get the space telescope to capture a light source that faint, engineers effectively gave it a 'pair of glasses'; in doing so, they were guided by Einstein's general theory of relativity, which stated that massive objects such as stars and galaxies can bend the path of light around them, in much the same way as a glass lens redirects light rays. The galaxy cluster Abell 2218, a relatively close 2 billion lightyears from Earth, was used like a giant magnifying glass or 'gravitational lens' to reveal the presence of the primitive stars behind it.

planetary systems in the process of forming in the Milky Way, or even giant star clusters lying beyond the bounds of our universe. Seeking a definitive answer, George Hale embarked on the construction of the world's first truly giant telescope. Equipped with a primary mirror 1.52m in diameter, it came into operation in 1909 on the summit of Mount Wilson in California. Nine years later, the Hooker Telescope, with a 2.5m mirror, was inaugurated at the same site. At the time, it was the largest in the world, and was capable of capturing the light from stars a million times weaker than the faintest star visible to the naked eye. In 1924 Edwin Hubble used this telescope to observe individual stars within nebulae; he concluded that they were indeed galaxies, immense concentrations of stars much like our Milky Way, but situated way beyond. The frontiers of space were being pushed back with dizzying speed. George Hale's last giant telescope, the 5.1m reflecting telescope at Mount Palomar Observatory, came into service in 1948, ten years after his death.

Clear air
The giant telescopes of the Cerro Paranal observatory (top), known collectively as the VLTI, are situated high above the Pacific Ocean in the bleak and arid Atacama Desert, far from any source of light pollution. The VLTI produced this image of the Crab Nebula (above), which lies at least 6,500 lightyears from Earth.

False mirrors

From 1950 to the 1980s, the world's major observatories acquired ever larger telescopes, sited far away from built-up areas to avoid interference from light pollution. Locating the telescopes at altitude helped to keep atmospheric disturbance from temperature variations or movements in layers of air to a minimum. Deserts in particular have many nights with no cloud cover. Accordingly, a series of observatories were opened in remote desert or mountain locations: Atacama (Chile, 1957), Arecibo (Puerto Rico, 1963), Mauna Kea (Hawaii, 1967) and La Silla (Chile, 1969).

The trend for ever-larger telescopes soon ran up against the problem of mirror size. In order to gather light in the best conditions, the surface of the mirror needs to be perfectly smooth. But the bigger a mirror becomes, the greater the likelihood of it deforming under its own weight. In addition, the polishing process, designed to remove slight imperfections on the surface and therefore accurate to within a micron, becomes increasingly problematic with size. As a result, the cost of such mirrors skyrocketed; beyond 10m in diameter, they were simply unaffordable.

In the 1970s astronomers such as the Americans Mike Johnson, Al Betz and Charles Towns of Berkeley University, California, and the Frenchman Antoine Labeyrie, began to investigate optimal interferometry as an alternative to massive mirrors. By combining the images received by two telescopes set at some distance from one another, it is possible to obtain a single image whose resolution is identical to that of a telescope whose diameter equals the distance between the two. Experiments were carried out throughout the 1980s, but the world's major observatories only really started to adopt the technology in the early 1990s. Nowadays, most observatories incorporate an optical interferometer.

Another method of boosting the size of mirrors without actually manufacturing larger ones was to create false mirrors made up of a

Starry night
The twin Keck I and Keck II telescopes, perched at an altitude of more than 4,200m on the slopes of Mauna Kea, a dormant volcano on Hawaii, occupy one of the best sites in the world for astronomical observation. These telescopes pioneered the era of segmented mirrors, and can observe visible light and infrared radiation equally well. Each telescope weighs 300 tonnes.

INTERFEROMETRY

This technology enables astronomers to enhance the resolution of an image by combining the light from several telescopes. To achieve this, different images are pieced together by means of a complex system of mirrors. Light can be seen as a wave spreading through space. Yet two waves meeting one another can either cancel one another out or combine to form a larger wave, depending on whether they are in phase or not. The mirror system is there to ensure that the images are put in phase. Just a fraction of the light received from a star is used to create the final image. Interferometry can produce very high resolution images, but requires objects that are bright enough in the first place in order to do so. Also, as the field of vision is limited, so the technique is more often used to study a particular star than to explore deep space.

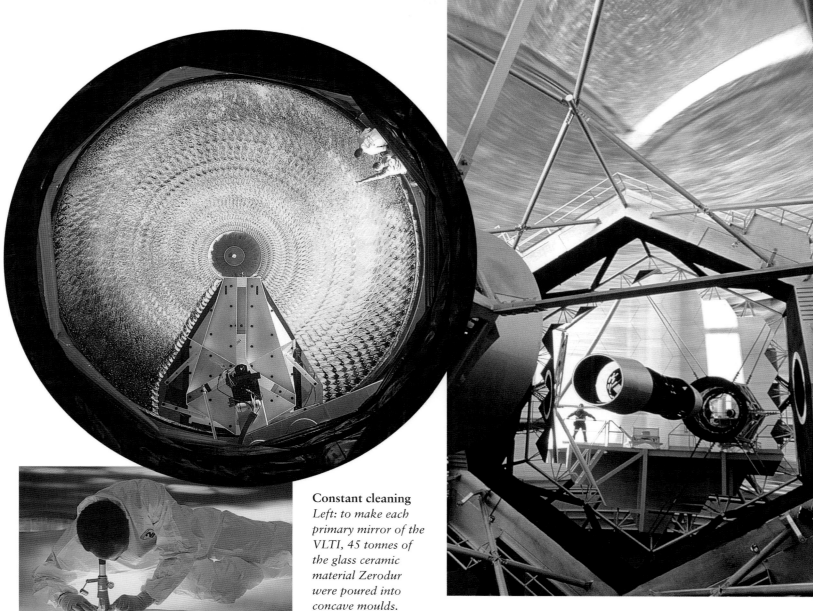

Constant cleaning
Left: to make each primary mirror of the VLTI, 45 tonnes of the glass ceramic material Zerodur were poured into concave moulds. Technicians constantly examined the surface to eradicate scratches, bubbles and any other minute imperfections.

Precision polishing
Top left: creating the mirrors for the Gemini telescopes, which will be installed at Mauna Kea and Cerro Pachon. Each will be polished to an accuracy of a few nanometres.

Hawaiian stargazer
Top right: the primary mirror of the Keck II telescope is composed of 36 smaller hexagonal mirrors, each 1.8m across.

multitude of small mirrors. The Keck telescopes, which came into service on Mauna Kea in Hawaii in 1993, were a key milestone for this technology. For the first time, a single huge mirror was replaced by a number of small hexagonal mirrors – 36 in total. The total assemblage, which measured 10m in diameter, was supported by 108 screwjacks and fitted with 168 pressure sensors, which twice a second work out the position of each hexagonal segment relative to its neighbour, in order to constantly optimise the mirror's overall shape. The second Keck telescope, constructed on the same principle, was installed at the site in 1996.

To the ends of the universe

Since the 1980s astronomical observation has been refined by technical innovations. One of the most important is the CCD (Charge-Coupled Device) camera for capturing

ADAPTIVE OPTICS

When the light from a distant star passes through Earth's atmosphere, it undergoes a considerable deviation. Temperature differences between layers of air alter the path of the light rays emitted by the object being observed. This means that, in one and the same image, some of the rays will arrive later than others. Adaptive optics consists of using a small deformable mirror controlled in real time by a computer: this synchronises all the light rays from the image so that they strike the primary mirror simultaneously. This means that astronomers on Earth can capture an almost identical image to that which they would have obtained in space.

the light from distant stars. The technology is radically different from the photographic plates used hitherto. The light received from stars is commuted by the CCD cells into an electronic signal, which is enhanced on a

THE COLOURS OF THE UNIVERSE

Light can be considered as either a wave or as particles endowed with energy – or with a wavelength – that is responsible for its colour. In terms of energy, astronomers can view the cosmos either in wavelengths that have more energy than visible light rays – UV, X-rays and gamma rays – or ones with less (infrared, radio waves) by fitting their telescopes with appropriate sensors. Each colour reveals a different facet of the Universe. The immense clouds of cold hydrogen that fill the galaxy emit radio waves that are received by radiotelescopes. Stars in the process of forming give off heat into the clouds of gas and dust from which they originated and in doing so emit infrared radiation. The study of ultraviolet light gives astronomers an insight into the dynamics of the gases of which stars are made. As for X-rays and gamma rays, these are used to study the most violent phenomena of the universe, such as supernovae and black holes.

Far, far away
Galaxy cluster Abell 520, some 2.4 billion lightyears from Earth in the constellation of Orion (above), was observed through gravitational lensing.

Dark horse
The Horsehead nebula (above right) is some 1,400 lightyears from Earth.

computer, cleansed of extraneous noise and stored. Far less bulky than photographic plates, the cameras are also easier to operate and, above all, are sensitive to wavelengths other than that of visible light. This allows them to observe the universe across a huge range of wavelengths. CCD technology has become indispensable in astronomy.

Meanwhile, the technique of adaptive optics, developed around the same time, has enabled astronomers to minimise disturbances caused by the Earth's atmosphere.

Prior to the 1980s, telescopes using photographic plates rarely gave astronomers the opportunity to see further than a billion lightyears away. Nowadays, giant telescopes have ranges ten times greater, and the boundaries are being pushed back all the time. The VLTI, for instance, can observe primitive

THE HYPERTELESCOPE

Discovering the continents on a planet orbiting a star other than our Sun; probing the giant black hole at the centre of our Galaxy – these are just two of the tantalising prospects offered by an ambitious space telescope project dreamt up by Antoine Labeyrie: the hypertelescope or EEI ('Exo-Earth Imager'). The plan is to make a huge instrument from 150 individual space telescopes, each equipped with a mirror 3m across. Using the principle of interferometry, this cluster of telescopes would together make up an instrument with a virtual mirror some 150km in diameter. Its cost, estimated at 10 billion euros, is extremely high for an optical instrument, but it represents a drop in the ocean compared to manned space missions like the Apollo programme. The hypertelescope may well be the only way of finding out whether life exists on another planet. A far smaller, ground-based prototype called Carlina, designed to test the basic principle behind the EEI, is currently under development at an observatory in the south of France. Its mirrors will be installed in the base of a natural depression and beam the light from stars back to a focal sphere floating in the sky above it, suspended from a balloon.

galaxies some 12 billion light years away. The Big Bang singularity, which at the same time represents both the birth of the universe and the limit of what is observable, is thought to have taken place around 13.7 billion years ago. This means that it is impossible to see further than the distance travelled by light during this time, namely 13.7 billion light years. Astronomers are very close to this limit. The next generation of telescopes will no doubt be able to observe the birth of the very first galaxies emerging from the primordial gas during the great chaos that marked the beginnings of our universe.

Keeping watch
The control room of the Gran Telescopio Canaria (GTC), sited on the island of Las Palmas in the Canaries (above right).

THE END OF ANTIMATTER

One of the fundamental principles of physics is that matter and antimatter were created in equal quantities and perfect symmetry during the Big Bang. Thus, each particle has an antiparticle and every proton has an antiproton. But in the course of experiments conducted in 2010 by Fermilab in Chicago – home of the most powerful particle collider before the advent of Europe's Large Hadron Collider (LHC) at CERN in Geneva – physicists established that there were 1 per cent fewer antiparticles than particles. In other words, the symmetry of the universe was imperfect. It followed, then, that antimatter had been seeping away over the 13.7 billion years since the birth of the universe. This may explain why the universe is not inundated with the gamma rays that always ensue when particles and antiparticles collide. It is also a fundamental reason why matter prevailed and our universe came into being.

Big eye on the sky
An artist's impression of the European Extremely Large Telescope (E-ELT), due to come into operation in 2018 near the existing Paranal Observatory in Chile. The E-ELT will have a primary mirror 42m in diameter, made up of 1,000 separate segments.

GLOBAL WARMING
Our planet in peril

The terms of the Kyoto Protocol, which was adopted in 1997 and came into force in 2005, commit the 183 signatory countries to reducing their greenhouse gas emissions. This agreement was reached after governments finally heeded the advice of climatologists, who had long been warning of accelerating global warming and pointing to human activities as the likely cause.

Melting away
The Perito Moreno glacier in Patagonia, southern Argentina (top right). Global warming has caused drastic shrinkage of the world's glaciers. Since 1850, glaciers in the European Alps have lost some 30 to 40 per cent of their surface area and about half of their volume. Samples of Antarctic ice can tell scientists a great deal about climate change. Drilling down into the icecap is like drilling back in time, reaching ice formed in previous years: this sample (right) is from 1819.

Ever since the first international conference on climate change, held in Geneva in 1979, the curves on graphs charting annual temperatures around the world have shown a persistent upward trend. The average has increased by 0.8°C since 1860, the first date for which regular readings are available, at least for the Northern hemisphere. Of this rise, some 0.55°C is accounted for by the period since 1950 alone. With the great improvements in measuring instruments over this time, plus the advent of satellites providing data on the Earth's atmosphere and its surface that are both more accurate and more universal than ever before, the inescapable conclusion is that every decade appears to be hotter than the preceding one.

Palaeoclimatologists have certainly shown that the whole of Earth's history has been characterised by alternating spells of glaciation (recurrent ice ages, marked by advancing glaciers, the sea receding and a drier climate) and interglacial periods (hotter and more humid conditions). But since around 13,500 years ago, the planet has entered a phase of generally increasing temperature – though this itself has not been immune from some significant anomalies. The period from around AD 850 to 1300, for example, experienced a milder episode known as the Medieval Climate Optimum (or Medieval Warm Period) which allowed the Vikings to colonise Greenland. There then ensued a Little Ice Age, which lasted until 1850, bringing temperatures at least 1°C colder on average, the cause of many ruined

---

TOO LATE TO SAVE GAIA?

In 1970, the British climate scientist James Lovelock formulated his 'Gaia' hypothesis, which claimed that all living organisms on Earth regulate the atmosphere's climate and chemistry in such a way as to promote and sustain life on the planet. Later, others confirmed the existence of mechanisms by which the biosphere keeps the Earth's climate stable and favourable. According to Lovelock, the pollution and despoliation resulting from an excessively dense human population have disrupted these natural processes to a critical degree. Gaia – the Earth as a single living ecosystem – has been so gravely damaged by this development that, he argues, humanity must prepare for the worst.

THE GREENHOUSE EFFECT

As the Earth is heated by the Sun, it radiates heat. More than half of this thermal radiation is lost in space, but a portion of it is trapped by water molecules, gases and particulates in the atmosphere and reflected back onto the Earth's surface. This is the 'greenhouse effect', first described in 1824 by French physicist Joseph Fourier. It is generally beneficial: without it, the Earth's mean temperature would be –18°C rather than +15°C. In 1896 the Swedish chemist Svante Arrhenius first suggested that burning fossil fuels might be amplifying the greenhouse effect, so raising the Earth's temperature by several degrees.

began in 1957. At that stage, it stood at 315ppm (parts per million) per unit of volume. By 2006 that figure had risen to 380ppm. Bubbles of air trapped in the Antarctic ice, which form an historical record of the variations in the composition of the atmosphere throughout the millennia, indicate that such a high level of CO_2 is without precedent for at least the past 650,000 years.

This build-up can be traced back to the Industrial Revolution, as a result of which fossil fuels such as coal, oil and natural gas became the driving force behind economic growth. Burning fossil fuels is the principal source of CO_2 emissions, followed by deforestation. The growth and intensification of agricultural activity have also had the effect of raising levels of nitrous oxide, produced by chemical fertilisers, and of methane, given off primarily by paddyfields and herds of grazing cattle.

Few serious scientists still deny the reality of global warming, but a number of climate

Choking the planet
A computer-generated map of the world shows the distribution of carbon dioxide released from the combustion of fossil fuels (below). The map was created using country statistics of natural gas, crude oil and coal consumption for 1987, the year the Montreal Protocol was signed. It is estimated that the emissions prevented by this protocol amount to the equivalent of 8 billion tonnes of CO_2.

harvests. Even so, no team of researchers has discovered any period over the last two millennia that was as hot as the 40 years between 1970 and 2010.

Humanity at fault

In 1941 the Yugoslav geophysicist Milutin Milankovic was the first to establish a causal link between long-term climatic fluctuations and the variations, also cyclical, in the movement of the Earth around the Sun. But Milankovic also found that current global warming had an unexpected origin: greenhouse gas emissions produced by human activities.

Systematic measuring of the concentration of carbon dioxide (CO_2) in the atmosphere, mainly comprised of greenhouse gases (GHGs),

Unnatural activity
Intensive cattle ranching in Texas (below). In 2006 a report by the UN's Food and Agriculture Organisation (FAO) confirmed that cattle were responsible for 37 per cent of methane emissions traceable to human activities.

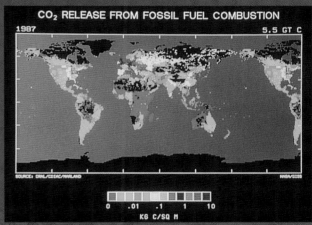

CO₂ RELEASE FROM FOSSIL FUEL COMBUSTION
1987   5.5 GT C
SOURCE: ORNL/CDIAC/MARLAND   NASA/GISS
0   .01   .1   1   10
KG C/SQ M

Fighting for breath
In China (above), now the world's worst industrial polluter, economic growth has eclipsed the Kyoto Protocol. In Paris (above right), when air pollution is especially bad, emergency measures restrict drivers to using their cars on alternate days.

sceptics still maintain that human activities are not at the root of the problem, or seek to play down their significance. The main plank of their argument is that the phenomenon is caused by increased solar activity. But when climatologists applied their models to preindustrial data, the only way they could obtain results that were at all commensurate with the present known increase in CO_2 levels was if the primary influence was attributed to the greenhouse effect, no matter how major a role was ascribed to solar influence.

The correlation between the growth in the concentration of human-produced greenhouse gases in the atmosphere and the rise in mean temperatures corresponds neatly with what we know about the greenhouse effect. Indeed, in its last report, prepared in 2007 (the next is due in 2014), the Intergovernmental Panel on Climate Change (IPCC) broadly concluded that the latter was in all likelihood caused by the former.

THE WORK OF THE IPCC

Founded in 1988 by the World Meteorological Organisation (WMO) and the United Nations Environment Programme (UNEP), the Intergovernmental Panel on Climate Change (IPCC) evaluates scientific data on changes to the world's climate. The panel is divided into three working parties, each of which comprises 100 scientists from various countries. These bodies collate and review the work of more than 2,500 climatologists, whose projections are based on 20 different climate models. Combining this information with technical and socioeconomic data, every six or seven years the IPCC draws up potential climatic scenarios that factor in conflicting hypotheses on population growth, economic development and technological progress. These are then presented to the political decision-makers.

An uncertain future

While many questions still remain unanswered about the complex mechanism that is our climate, the first effects of global warming are already apparent. Scientists are deeply alarmed by the rate at which glaciers have melted since the 1990s, far faster than anyone anticipated. In many regions glaciers provide the major source of fresh water, while the melting process is contributing directly to a rise in global sea level. It is also disrupting normal circulation in the world's oceans and impairing the sea's ability to absorb CO_2, further exacerbating global warming. This is because the polar icecaps reflect back some 90 per cent of the light they receive from the Sun, while the sea absorbs most of it. Yet even the vast glacial icecaps covering Greenland and Antarctica are beginning to dwindle. If this process continues, or worse accelerates, it could cause a dramatic rise in sea levels.

The majority of the world's population lives on or near the coast. Some communities have already been displaced by rising seawater levels, from the inhabitants of Tuvalu in the South Pacific to those in the Charente and the Vendée on the Atlantic coast of France. Coastal communities also bear the brunt of cyclones. The most violent tropical storms, those listed as category 4 or 5, are on the increase. All the available evidence points to a marked intensification of the water cycle and a greater incidence of heatwaves. It also appears that the El Niño event, a periodic reversal in the currents carrying water masses between the eastern and western Pacific, which brings devastating rainfall to some areas and drought to others, is recurring with greater frequency. Despite all these warning signs, the relative rarity and shortness of extreme weather events,

MODELLING THE CLIMATE

The ways in which the world's climate might evolve are predicted in mathematical models of the planet's climate system. The Earth is first divided up into a grid pattern, with each section a few tens of kilometres wide and several hundred kilometres high. Climatologists plot into this three-dimensional framework the physical parameters governing the climate, as well as all other relevant data, in order to obtain as accurate as possible a representation of the Earth, from the speed of its axial rotation to the distribution of its vegetation and ice floes. They then factor in disruptions to see how these affect the overall dynamics of the system. There is much room for improvement in current modelling. For instance, the grid is still too coarse to take account of very localised phenomena, such as storms or seaspouts. Furthermore, clouds, which remain poorly understood, are responsible for some 70 to 80 per cent of the discrepancies between the results of the different models. Constant improvements are ongoing; encouragingly, when these models have been tested on past climatic conditions, they have proved reasonably accurate.

as well as the lack of data from the pre-satellite era, mean that it is still extremely difficult to determine whether these phenomena are indicative of an underlying trend.

Farming, the first casualty of climatic disaster, is witnessing a fundamental disruption of its ancient rhythms, as the time when crops ripen and need to be harvested arrives earlier every year. Thousands of field studies confirm that animals and birds are migrating earlier, and that the range of distribution of some

Climatic catastrophes
In 2009 a typhoon devastated the region around the Philippine capital Manila, bringing the worst flooding seen there for 40 years (above). The disaster made some 500,000 people homeless. The natural world is also badly affected by such extreme events. Tarawa Atoll in the Pacific, which is threatened by rising sea levels, is becoming a graveyard of coconut palms (left). Before long, the people living there may have no choice but to move elsewhere.

Vital resource
In March 2010 the southwestern Chinese province of Yunnan was affected by the worst drought to hit the country for a century. By the end of that month 24 million people were estimated to be without clean drinking water.

Scorched earth
A dried-up riverbed in Yunnan province during the drought of March 2010 (below). Just three months later, torrential rain caused the worst floods for a decade in nearby Hubei province.

species is shifting towards more northerly climes and higher altitudes – including disease-bearing species such as the mosquito *Aedes aegypti*, the vector of dengue fever. The fate of the polar bear, whose hunting season grows ever shorter as the summer pack ice in the Arctic steadily shrinks, has become a powerful symbol for the danger that global warming poses to many animal species. Some regions may benefit in the short term from milder climatic conditions, but climate models

indicate that ultimately the entire world will be affected by a shortage of fresh water. No doubt the climate system has several other unpleasant surprises in store. For example, huge quantities of carbon and methane are currently trapped within the permafrost (the deep layer of frozen soil within the Arctic Circle); when this melts – a process that is already underway – it could reach a point where these gases will be released en masse, further hastening global warming.

Kyoto and beyond

While taking into account a number of uncertainties – such as the accuracy of the scientific projections and the trajectory of economic growth – the IPCC estimates that the rise in average temperature by the 2090s could be in the order of 1.8°C to 4°C higher than mean temperatures in the period from 1980 to 1999. The effects of global warming could only be sustainable by the human population, not to mention other species, if that increase is kept below 2°C. This figure requires that the concentration of CO_2 in the Earth's atmosphere does not rise beyond 350ppm. To achieve this target, global emissions from now until 2050 will have to be reduced to half of what they were in 1990.

Deforestation danger
Huge swathes of the Amazonian rainforest have been cleared for ranching and the intensive cultivation of soya beans, as here in Mato Grosso in Brazil. This factor alone is responsible for around a 25 per cent rise in CO_2 emissions. At the Copenhagen summit in December 2009, President Lula of Brazil pledged to cut his country's deforestation programme by 40 per cent by 2020.

The Kyoto Protocol, which was signed in 1997 with the notable exception of the world's largest economy, the United States, only came into force in 2005. This agreement was meant to produce an average reduction of 5.2 per cent in greenhouse gases by 2010. In the event, emissions increased by 40 per cent between 1990 and 2009. A new agreement is due to supersede Kyoto in 2012. Technological measures designed to bring about a reduction in GHGs include research into renewable energy sources, the development of hybrid and fuel-cell-powered vehicles, and carbon burial.

CARBON BURIAL

A number of pilot installations have been testing the new technology of carbon-dioxide capture. The gas is captured at the point of emission from power stations, cement works and other heavy CO_2 producers, then buried in deep saline aquifers (permeable rocks holding salt water), or in abandoned natural gas and oil wells and deep coal seams. Geologists are adamant the technique is reliable, but the main obstacle to its full implementation, apart from the high cost, is the difficulty of persuading local communities of the safety of subterranean pockets of CO_2. Investment in hundreds or even thousands of such installations could reduce GHG emissions by 15 per cent by the target date of 2050.

In addition, various economic measures aim to persuade companies and households to reduce their carbon footprint. In 2005 the EU introduced its Emission Trading Scheme, which allows large CO_2 emitters to buy preset quotas of emissions from the cleanest industries (so incentivising reductions). The Kyoto Protocol also put in place a mechanism for transferring 'green' technology from industrialised nations to less developed countries, while an international accord was reached to reduce deforestation by half.

On a planet with finite resources, many agencies highlight the unsustainability of the traditional model of continuing growth in the production and consumption of material goods. Their premise is that society should be reconstituted on an entirely different footing.

Speaking out
Demonstrators against unsustainable growth gather outside the Copenhagen summit in 2009 (above). At this rally Kumi Naidu, the director of Greenpeace International, claimed that global warming costs the lives of some 300,000 people every year.

From paper to screen

Written works are following the inexorable trend of our age from the real to the virtual. This is fundamentally changing the reader's relationship with the text, and redefining the traditional model of how knowledge is generated and disseminated.

The book is undergoing its own digital revolution, perhaps signalling an end to the pleasures of paper and holding a printed book in the hand. The first electronic book, the Rocket eBook, appeared in 1998 in Silicon Valley, California. With a format almost the same size as a paperback, this digital reader looked as alien as a UFO at a time when portable computers and personal digital assistants were still at the cutting edge of IT hardware. Its high price ($500) and limited storage capacity soon condemned it to the scrapheap of good ideas.

Even so, this early failure marked the beginning of a line of development for the

New and old
NuvoMedia's Rocket eBook, shown here (left) with Alice in Wonderland *on its screen, was the first such device to come on the market, sold in the US by Barnes & Noble. Below: rolls of paper at a print works – the traditional printed book is still being bought by readers, but for how much longer?*

Luckily for Alice, the little magic bottle had now had its full effect, and she grew no larger; still it was very uncomfortable, and, as there seemed to

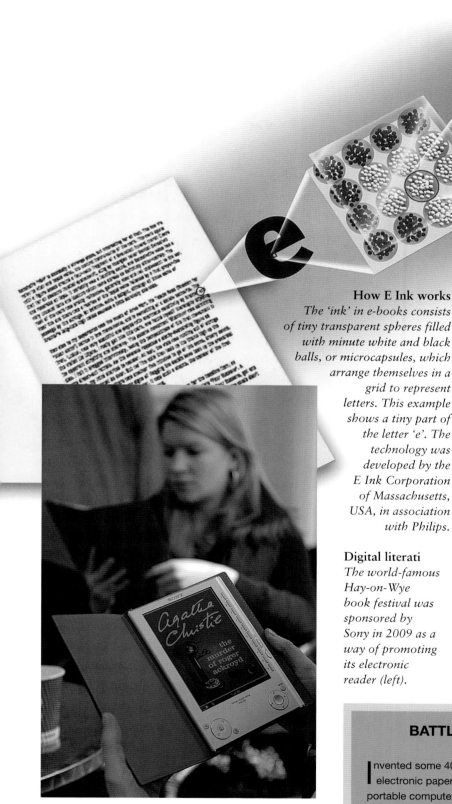

How E Ink works
The 'ink' in e-books consists of tiny transparent spheres filled with minute white and black balls, or microcapsules, which arrange themselves in a grid to represent letters. This example shows a tiny part of the letter 'e'. The technology was developed by the E Ink Corporation of Massachusetts, USA, in association with Philips.

Digital literati
The world-famous Hay-on-Wye book festival was sponsored by Sony in 2009 as a way of promoting its electronic reader (left).

Sony shows the way

Then, in 2004, Sony's LIBRIé broke new ground in using E Ink, a kind of electronic paper, in place of the traditional LCD (liquid crystal display) screen. This innovation meant that the reader used less energy and was also lighter to hold than previous models. Although the LIBRIé was only launched in Japan, it sparked interest and two years later was rolled out worldwide as the Sony Reader. This had a more ergonomic design and, in the USA and Canada, an expanding catalogue of digitised books which helped it to achieve moderately impressive sales.

Electronic ink is a flexible medium made up of billions of tiny spheres the diameter of a human hair. Each of these contains white pigments, with a positive charge, and black pigments, with a negative one. When a current is applied underneath a sphere, the white pigments are drawn towards the top, while the black ones remain at the bottom – or vice-versa. As a result, each sphere shows either a white or a black face. The magnetic field running through the page forms the characters, words, sentences and images. Placed between rigid supports, this page constitutes the surface of an electronic book display. The process

electronic book, with new models – the SoftBook, the Every Book, the Cybook, the Gemstar – being launched at regular intervals. None of these interim technologies had a long shelf life or enjoyed much success. All failed to capture the public's imagination or corner the market – either due to their cost, or the small number of digitised works then being issued by publishers, or perhaps the simple fact that they were unappealing to use.

BATTLE OF THE ELECTRONIC PAPER MANUFACTURERS

Invented some 40 years ago in the Xerox Corporation laboratories, electronic paper is at the heart of a major industrial battle. Just as for portable computer screens, whose manufacture is concentrated in a very limited number of firms, the creation of electronic reader screens taps into an expertise that is not widespread. Bridgestone, E Ink, Epson, LG and Plastic Logic are the principal players. These manufacturers supply Amazon, Bookeen, Hewlett-Packard, MSI, Sony and Samsung with their e-book screens, along with myriad products made in Southeast Asia. E Ink is one of a small range of technologies employed in electronic paper. Alternatives include BiNem developed by the French Nemoptic company: this uses liquid crystal technology to give a high-resolution image with strong contrast that the company claims makes reading an e-book as comfortable as scanning a traditional page of printed text.

Not-so-green option

An online edition of the German daily Die Welt (right). If online newspapers take off, it will drastically reduce the amount of newspaper that ends up in recycling (above). Some have hailed the e-book as an environmentally friendly device. But studies have estimated that the annual carbon footprint of an e-reader is 250kg of CO_2, whereas that of equivalent paper resources is just 1kg.

relies on electrophoresis, a technique chiefly used in biology based on the displacement of ions under the influence of an electrical field.

Marketing and legal considerations

Thereafter, the electronic book industry did grow, but still remained fairly marginal. Marketing executives hoped that it would emulate the runaway success of another single-function device, the mobile phone. But whether for reasons concerning the content on offer, or the price, the market for the e-book still failed to take off. At a time when more and more homes were becoming equipped with computers, people seemed to have little interest in acquiring a very specific piece of equipment, and very few book publishers were attracted to the idea of converting their business to electronic media.

The rights of authors opened up a whole new realm of potentially insurmountable pitfalls. Publishers did not, in all cases, have the rights to use an author's works on electronic media, and hoped to avoid engaging in long and costly negotiations with the rights owners before they could reach a settlement. At the same time, just as in the music industry, they were alarmed by the potential for electronic piracy of works on their list. This clear case of 'cold feet' on the part of the publishing industry did little to stimulate the makers of e-books to turn out more units or, as a result of greater numbers, to lower the

TOWARDS THE DIGITAL NEWSPAPER?

Most newspapers now offer their content as an online resource, either free or by subscription. Although it is possible to access this as an Internet download on, say, tablet-sized screens like an iPad, manufacturers like Amazon are now looking at specially dedicated portable devices with larger screens. Beyond this, technology is being developed that will dispense with a rigid reader altogether: the flexible electronic-paper screen. Around 0.3mm thick (twice that of traditional newsprint) and roughly the size of a tabloid (25 x 40cm), these screens consist of a layer of electronic ink on a metal-foil substrate containing extremely thin electronic circuitry. An RFID microchip enables the device to regularly download new content; no battery is required. This may herald the dawn of fully digital newspapers.

price of their product. This created a vicious circle in which the consumer quite simply seemed to have been left out of the reckoning.

Looking for the breakthrough

In 2006 there was yet another attempt to invigorate the e-book market with the launch of various new models. Readers became slimmer, lighter and were produced in an A4 format. To make the reader interface more intuitive, screens now replicated the turning of a physical page. This new generation of devices could run for more than a week without recharging, while WiFi models facilitated wireless use. One model, Irex Technologies' iLiad Electronic Reader, even allowed users to annotate documents they were reading. Meanwhile, the Sony Reader, an upgraded version of the LIBRIé, came on the market in that same year. The following year, 2007, saw the arrival of Amazon's Kindle; this online bookstore teamed the launch of its reader with a catalogue of almost 250,000 digitised titles, most of which were around 30 per cent cheaper than their paper counterparts. The first colour-screen reader appeared in 2009.

But for all this technological progress, the place of this gadget in modern society still seems unclear. The multimedia possibilities of the electronic book excites designers and seduces users, but the big stumbling block remains the limited availability of works, which comes back to the thorny problem of authors' rights. The United States leads the fields in the number of digitised titles on offer, primarily from the Amazon and Barnes & Noble websites, not forgetting the global offensive by Google, which to date has digitised almost 12 million books and made them available in PDF format, potentially readable by all models of e-book currently on sale.

E-books can be downloaded and read anywhere. This flexibility of use goes hand-in-hand with a new services: in 2010, Apple's iPad

Pocket library
Although it is just 1cm thick and weighs only 220g, the Sony reader (2010) can hold 350 full-length books.

TALKING BOOK
Many of the latest generation of e-book readers come equipped with text-to-speech software to read the text aloud for visually impaired or dyslexic people.

broke new ground by combining an e-book reading facility with almost all the functions of a small computer. With Apple's legendary design and marketing flair, this device seems to point the way forward for the e-book, potentially achieving the breakthrough into a mass market. In a sign of these changing times, at Christmas 2009 for the first time Amazon sold more electronic books than their paper equivalents. At the moment, given licensing difficulties, the traditional book is holding its own; but if the rights issues are resolved, the e-book seems set to take its place.

Versatile platform
Apple's iPad (2010) is not just a multimedia e-reader, it can also be used as a games console and as a device for surfing the Web, all in a tablet format weighing just 700g. It can operate for 10 hours without recharging.

PRINT ON DEMAND

Traditional publishing now has the cost-effective option of 'print on demand' (POD) at its disposal. The advent of digital printing gave rise to this facility, which dispenses with print-runs (and the costly drawbacks of warehousing and remaindering) by only printing copies of a book once an order has been received. Academic publishers in particular (including university presses) use POD services to maintain large backlists of sometimes obscure titles.

The flying wing 2004

In 2002 Yves Rossy, a qualified pilot from Switzerland, had the idea of making a powered flying wing – a kind of hang-glider with jet engines. To realise this ambitious dream, he got in touch with a German company, JetCat, which specialised in building jet engines for flying scale models of aircraft. Carrying the powerplants was a carbon-fibre wing with a span of 3m, made by ACT Composites of Geneva. The wing was foldable, so it could be carried on board a light plane.

On 24 June, 2004, Rossy jumped from a small Pilatus aircraft flying at an altitude of 4,000m over the airfield at Yverdon in Switzerland. After a few seconds of free-fall, he deployed his wings and began a controlled glide. Some 2,500m above the ground, he ignited his two jet engines and waited a short while until they stabilised. Then he opened the throttles and flew horizontally for four minutes at a speed of 180km/h, in formation alongside the Pilatus.

Is it a bird? Is it a plane?
Yves Rossy's invention made him history's first 'Jetman', capable of flying like a bird with a minimum of apparatus. The pilot steers the flying wing simply by shifting his weight.

Crossing the Channel

Adapting his wing to carry four engines, Rossy crossed the English Channel on 26 September, 2008, almost a century after Louis Blériot. The crossing took just under ten minutes, flying at almost 300km/h at altitudes of between 800 and 1,000m. His modified wing had a span of just 2.5m and weighed only 60kg (half of it fuel). His four standard JetCat P200 engines each generated 22kg of thrust. In 2009 Rossy attempted to fly across the Straits of Gibraltar, but failed due to technical problems.

Rossy is hoping to develop his flying wing and market it to extreme sports enthusiasts. He is adamant that only experienced pilots should attempt to fly this thrilling but potentially dangerous machine.

JETMAN – THE NEW ICARUS

Yves Rossy was born in Neuchâtel in Switzerland on 27 August, 1959. He became a jet fighter pilot at the age of 20, and in eight years of flying chalked up more than 1,000 hours flying Mirage IIIs. He then joined Swissair, moving from co-pilot to captain on Airbus A-320s by 2000. He has made more than 1,000 parachute jumps and is also skilled in aerobatics, hang-gliding and paragliding.

YouTube 2005

Created in February 2005 by three former employees of the internet money-transfer site PayPal, YouTube is a video-sharing site where users can post, host and view amateur videos from all over the world. It soon became the main provider of online video clips.

By 2010 more than 6 billion clips had been viewed on the YouTube site, and it was estimated that 20 hours of new programming

Dancing Matt
Matt Harding, the American video game designer, became an Internet celebrity after posting videos on YouTube showing him dancing in front of famous landmarks around the world.

was uploaded every minute. The social impact of the site has been huge: aside from frivolous postings there have also been serious exposés of acts of brutality by dictatorial regimes. Because US law guarantees freedom of expression, some clips posted on the site have been shocking. It is now the fourth most-visited site on the Internet, behind Google, Yahoo! and Facebook.

VIRAL VIDEOS

Since the launch of YouTube, a number of videos on the site have 'gone viral', recording millions of hits. Some of the most popular are candid clips of the antics of children or animals, such as the 'Charlie Bit My Finger' series, showing a baby biting his toddler brother, and the 'Maru the Cat' videos, in which a Japanese owner's pet leaps wildly in and out of cardboard boxes. The German film *Downfall*, about the last days of Adolf Hitler, has also been the subject of many YouTube parodies, with new English subtitles depicting the fascist dictator ranting about (often trivial) present-day political and social issues.

Sudoku 2004

Inspired by the 'magic squares' published in newspapers in the 19th century, Sudoku is a puzzle which consists of filling out a grid using a series of numbers from 1 to 9. The grid comprises nine square 'regions' (or 'sub-grids'), denoted by heavier lines in which at east one number has been filled in. A complete sequence of numbers from 1 to 9 must be placed in each of these subdivisions; the same number cannot appear twice on a single line, in the same column, or within the same region.

The modern game of Sudoku was devised by a retired American architect Howard Garns, who published a grid he christened 'Number Place' in Dell Pencil Puzzles & Word Games magazine in May 1979. The first British Sudoku puzzle appeared in *The Times* on 12 November, 2004, and the game has been published there daily ever since. The newspaper also sends grids to the mobile phones of subscribers to its online service. So popular has the puzzle become that thousands of people now compete in annual Sudoku championships.

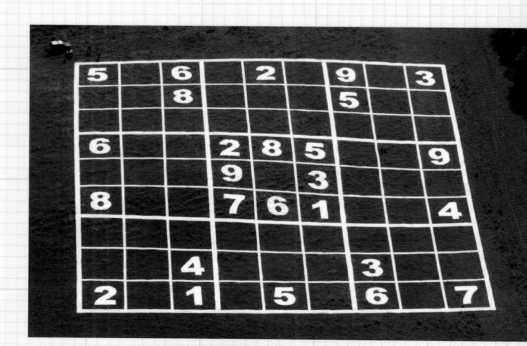

Grass grid *A giant Sudoku grid marked out on a hill by the M4 motorway near Bristol in 2005.*

2008-9

- Barack Obama becomes the first mixed-race US president (2008)
- Kosovo proclaims its independence (2008)
- US sub-prime mortgages spark a global economic crisis (2008–9)

• Synthetic 'gecko' adhesive is developed, mimicking the extraordinary sticking power of the gecko lizard; the glue effectiveness relies on carbon nanotubes and their electrical interactions with a surface

• Energy-generating flooring systems are installed in public places, transform the footfall of dancers or passers-by into electricity

• Switzerland halts its geothermal energy programme after drilling sets off earth tremors

• An interactive wallpaper equipped with touch sensors is trialled, enabling invisible circuits to be incorporated in the walls

• The final touches are put to a piece of cloth painstakingly woven from genuine spider-silk, a material more resistant than Kevlar® yet far lighter than steel

▼ Inside the tokamak for the ITER fusion reactor

2010

- International Year of Biodiversity announced by the UN
- Debt crisis in Greece sends economic tremors through Eurozone
- Explosion on drilling platform pollutes Gulf of Mexico with oil
- Volcanic explosion in Iceland causes air traffic chaos
- David Cameron heads coalition government in Britain

• Therapeutic trials are undertaken in the search for cures for neurodegenerative illnesses such as Alzheimer's and Parkinson's diseases involving, respectively, a vaccine and gene therapy

• Construction gets underway in southern France on ITER, the world's largest experimental nuclear fusion reactor

• Signatories to the 1992 Convention on Biodiversity are faced with the dispiriting knowledge that, even as they prepare to engage in the listing and conservation of species, the world is experiencing an alarming decline in biodiversity claimed by some scientists to be a sixth mass extinction

▼ Endangered species of cactus in the Joshua Tree National Park, California

▲ A forensic scientist in action

Index

Page numbers in *italics* refer to captions.

Picture credits

Front cover: main image: schoolchildren in rural China using the school's laptop, Corbis/Yi Lu. **Inset**: © All Canada Photos/Superstock. **Spine**: Color bright flash drive memory stick © Shutterstock/yadviga. **Back cover**: 'Jetman', Service de Presse Yves Rossy Jetman.
Page 2, left to right, top row: © Sustainable Dance Club – Sustainable Dance Floor™; Service de Presse Yves Rossy Jetman; Corbis/EPA/RBM Online; 2nd row: Cosmos/SSPL/Science Museum, London; Getty Images/Time and Life Images/ Urbano Delvalle; Getty Images/Business Wire; 3rd row: © ITER Organization; Jean-Pierre Delagarde; Cosmos/SPL/Mauro Fermariello; bottom row: AFP/Getty Images/China Photos; © Space Adventures Ltd; Rex Features.
Pages 4-5: Keren Su/Getty Images; 6t: Corbis/ Rémi Benali; 6b: Cosmos/SSPL/Science Museum; 6/7b: Age Fotostock/Stuart Pearce; 7t: Corbis/ Retna Ltd/Kabik; 7c: Réa/Raphaël Demaret; 7br: Getty Images/Business Wire; 8: Ciel et Espace Photos/JPL/University of Arizona/Nasa; 8bl: Double-Vue.fr/Pascal Goetgheluck; 8br: Bsip/Docktock/Emergency; 9t: Corbis/Niall Benvie; 9cr: © Toyota France; 9b: © Samsung; 10t: Photononstop/J.-C & D. Pratt; 10bl: BSIP/ Cardoso; 11t: Cosmos/SPL/Carl Goodman; 11bl: © Hamelin Digital 2005; 11br: Réa/Denis; 12tl: Sipa/Darpa; 12bl: AFP/IUCN/Brad Wilson; 12/13b: Réa/Laif/Daniel Rosenthal; 12t &13t: illustrations (see below); 13c: Réa/Wilfried Maisy; 13br: LookatSciences/Matteis; 14tl: Cosmos/ SPL/David Nunuk; 14b: AFP/Getty Images/Win McNamee; 14/15t: Réa/Ropi/ Featurechina/ Chun Lei; 15t: © Courtesy of Matt Harding; 15bl: AFP/Getty Images/Fabrice Coffrini; 15br: © Courtesy of Apple; 16tr: Cosmos/SPL/ André Geim; 16cl: © Sustainable Dance Club – Sustainable Dance Floor™; 16b: Réa/Ropi/ Antonio Pisacreta; 17t: Corbis/Science Faction/ Peter Ginter; 17b: Hemis.fr/Tao Images, architect: He Jingtang; 18/19: Ciel et Espace/ESO; 20tr: Cosmos/SSPL/Science Museum, London; 20bl: Cosmos/SPL/Volker Steger; 21 & 21b: Cosmos/ SPL/Navstar; 22t: Corbis/George Steinmetz; 22b: Double-Vue.fr/P. Psaïla; 23t: Cosmos/SPL/ Detlev van Ravenswaay; 24t: Corbis/Douglas Keister; 24br: Getty Images/UpperCut Images; 24bl: Réa/Richard Damoret; 25: Réa/The New York Times/Ko Sasaki; 26tl: Corbis/Brownie Harris; 26/27: Cosmos/SSPL/Science Museum, London; 26bl: Cosmos/SPL/Detlev van Ravenswaay; 26br: Cosmos/SPL/Friedrich Saurer; 27tr: Courtesy of the National Institute of Standards and Technology (NIST), USA; 27c: Réa/Wilfried Maisy; 27b: Corbis/EPA; 27br: Cosmos/SPL/Detlev van Ravenswaay; 28l: AFP/Colin McPherson; 28r: Corbis/Rémi Benali; 29t Réa/The New York Times/Andy Manis; 29b: Réa/Contrasto/Roberto Caccuri; 30t: Reuters/China Daily/CDIC; 30b: AFP/Cheryl Hatch; 31: illustrations (see below); 32/33t: Cosmos/SPL/Victor de Schwanberg;

32b: Collection Christophel/'The Island' directed by Michael Bay, 2004, Warner Bros; 33t: Cosmos/ SPL/James King Holmes; 33cr: Corbis/EPA/RBM Online; 33bl: Réa/Redux/Tony Law; 34tl: AFP/ AltoPress, Éric Audras; 34b: Réa/The New York Times/Wynn Thompson; 35t: Réa/The New York Times/ Redux/Sandy Huffaker; 35b: Age Fotostock/Stuart Pearce; 36t: Fedephoto/Vincent Leloup; 36b: Réa/Reporters/Claire Deprez; 37t: Réa/The New York Times/Redux/Zack Canepari; 37cr: Réa/François Henry; 38t: Getty Images/ Business Wire; 38b: Getty Images/Ho; 39t & 39b: Réa/Denis; 40t: Réa/Benoît Decout; 40b: Réa/ Panos/Jacob Silbergberg; 41t: Leemage/ Imagestate/Lee Frost; 41b: Réa/Raphaël Demaret; 42b: Cosmos/SPL/Detlev van Ravenswaay; 43t: Ciel et Espace Photos/JPL/University of Arizona/ NASA; 43b: Cosmos/Science Faction/Digital Version Copyright/NASA; 44/45: Corbis; 44bl: Corbis/ Bettmann; 45bl: Corbis; 45br: Cosmos/SPL/US Geological Survey; 46t: Corbis/EPA; 46c: Corbis/ Kinetikon Pictures/Michael Benson; 47tc: Cosmos/SPL/JPL Space Science Institute/NASA; 47t: Ciel et Espace/JPL/University of Arizona/ NASA; 47bl: Cosmos/SPL/NASA/JHU-APL/Asu/ Carnegie Institution of Washington; 48t: Signatures/Florence Brochoire; 48b: Corbis/Heide Benser; 49: Corbis/Retna Ltd/Kabik; 50t: Réa/ Redux/The New York Times/David R. Lutman; 50b: AFP/Valéry Hache; 51t: Cosmos/SPL/Sandia National Laboratories, Albuquerque, USA; 51b: Corbis/William Whitehurst; 52tr: Réa/The New York Times; 52b: AFP/Getty Images/Sean Gallup; 53tr: Cosmos/SPL/Paul Wootton; 53b: Double- Vue.fr/Pascal Goetgheluck; 54t: Getty Images/ Car Culture; 54b: © Porsche France; 55t: Réa/ Didier Maillac; 55b: © Toyota France; 56tl: Sipa/ Rex Features/David Lee; 56c: © Samsung; 56b: Sipa/Isopress/Sierakowski; 57: Réa/ Redux/Andy Kropa; 58t: Reuters/Mike Blake; 58b: © Courtesy of Apple; 59t: Bsip/Docktock/ Emergency; 59b: Corbis/Andrew Brookes; 60t: AFP/Esa; 60b: illustration (see below); 61t: © Courtesy of NASA; 61b: Cosmos/SPL/NASA/ESA/ STSCI/Hight-Z Supernova Search Team; 62t: illustration (see below); 62b: Réa/Hamilton; 63t: Jean-Pierre Delagarde; 63b: Corbis/Niall Benvie; 64t: The Picture Desk/Collection Dagli Orti/ Workshop of José Antonio Ortega and El Lledoner, Spain; 64b: Gamma Photo/Rapho/Michaël Yamashita; 65tl: Jean-Pierre Delagarde; 65tr: LookatSciences; 65b: Bsip/AltoPress/PhotoAlto; 66t: BSOP/ Cardoso; 66b: Corbis/Photocuisine/ P. Desgrieux; 67tr: Photononstop/Hervé de Gueltzl; 67b: BSIP/ Chassenet; 68t: Photononstop/ J.-C. & D. Pratt; 68b: illustration (see below); 69t: © Hamelin Digital 2005; 69b: © Anoto AB, 2007; 70/71b: Signatures/Bruno Ansellem; 70b: Corbis/Kelly-Mooney Photography; 71b: Réa/ Michel Gaillard; 72/73t: © Britannica; 72tr: © Larousse.fr; 72b: Réa/Denis; 7tc: © Encyclopédie Universalis; 73tr: © Wissen.de; 74t: Double-Vue.fr/Pascal Goetgheluck; 74b: Réa/Denis; 75t: Corbis/George Logan; 75br: Rue des Archives/BCA/Robert Voets; 76tl: Réa/Laif/

Peter Granser; 76tr: Réa/Ian Hanning; 77cr: Signatures/Sébastien Erome; 77bl: Cosmos/SPL/ Mauro Fermariello; 77br: Andia/Alpaca/E. Soudan; 78tl: Réa/L'Express/Valérie Dayan; 78tr & 78b: Cosmos/SPL/Mauro Fermariello; 79: Réa/ L'Express/Valérie Dayan; 80r: Cosmos/SPL/ESA/ ASI/S-Corvaja; 80b: Cosmos/SPL/NASA; 81t: AFP/Getty Images/Robyn Beck; 81c: AFP/Getty Images/Alexander Nemenov; 81b : © Space Adventures Ltd; 82t: Cosmos/SPL/Scaled Composites; 82b: Sipa/ WENN.COM/ZOB/CB2; 83t: Cosmos/SPL/Carl Goodman; 83cr: © Space Adventures Ltd; 84/85: Cosmos/Focus/Erich Speigelhalter; 84b: Cosmos/NHPA/Kevin Schafer; 85bl: AFP/IUCN/Kai Schuette; 86: Biosphoto/ B. Wright/OSF; 86cr: Cosmos/NHPA/Norbert Wu; 86b: Biosphoto/Peter Arnold/Thomas D. Mangelsen; 87t: AFP/ IUCN/Brad Wilson; 87b: Biosphoto/Panda Photo/ N. Maraspini; 88t: Réa/Hanning/Dod; 88cr: Corbis/David Howells; 89t: Getty Images/Check Six; 89b: Corbis/DPA/Peter Steffen; 90t: Corbis/ David Howells; 90cr: Getty Images/Ethan Miller; 90b: AFP/Getty Images/Michaël Kappeler; 91tl: AFP/ Ali Yussef; 91tr: AFP/Jewel Samad; 91b: Reuters; 92/93t: Collection Christophe/ 'Terminator Renaissance', 2009, Sony Pictures Releasing France; 92b: Corbis/EPA/Oliver Killig; 93: Sipa/ Darpa; 94cl: J. H. Editorial/Minden Pictures/Ingo Arndt; 94/95b: Réa/The New York Times/Michael Nagle; 95t: Cosmos/SPL/Bernhard Edmaier; 95br: Réa/Laif/Daniel Rosenthal; 96bl: © ADEME-BRGM, the principles of a geothermal heat pump; 96r: Urba Images Server/M. Gile; 97t: LookatSciences/ Bernard Martinez; 97b: Réa/Benoît Decout; 98cl: Sipa/AP/Marcio José Sanchez; 98r: Réa/ Redux/The New York Times/Peter Dasilva; 99t: Réa/Redux/Michael Rubenstein; 99r: Réa/ Wilfried Maisy; 100cl: Roger-Viollet/Albert Harlingue; 100/101t: Getty Images/Sharon Montrose; 100b: illustration (see below); 101b: Réa/Benoît Decout; 102/103t: Réa/HH/Mischa Keuser; 101tl: Cosmos/SPL/Chris Hellier; 102br: Cosmos/SPL/Victor de Schwanberg; 103tr: Cosmos/Philip Poupin; 103b: Cosmos/SPL/ Power and Syred; 104: Réa/The New York Times/ Ed Zurga; 105t: LookatSciences/ Matteis; 105b: LookatSciences/Frédéric Woirgard; 106t: © Nokia; 106b: AFP/PhotoAlto/James Hardy; 107tr: Reuters/ Stelios Varias; 107c: Rex Features; 107b: AFP/Getty Images/Christian Jakubaszek; 108t: Cosmos/SPL/Wellcome DCN; 108b: AFP/François Guillot; 109cr: Cosmos/SPL/ Torsten Wittmann; 109b: Cosmos/SPL/ Torsten Wittmann; 110t: illustrations (see below); 110b: Hemis.fr/Axiom Photographic Agency/E. Rowe; 111t: Cosmos/SPL/Wellcome DCN; 111c: BSIP/MBPL/Ian Hooton; 111bl: Cosmos/SPL/Alfred Pasieka; 112: AFP/Getty Images/Win McNamee; 113tl: BSIP/Science Source; 113cr: Réa/Ian Hanning; 113b: BSIP/ Phototake/Scott; 114bl: Cosmos/SPL/Science Museum, London; 114br: Corbis/Jim Sugar; 115t: Ciel et Espace/G Hüdepohl; 115cr: Cosmos/ SPL/ESO; 116: Cosmos/SPL; 117tl: Cosmos/SPL/ David Parker; 117tr: Cosmos/SPL/David Nunuk;

117cl: LookatSciences/Patrick Landmann; 118t: Cosmos/SPL/NASA/CXC/CFHT/A. Mahdavi, U. Vic; 118b: Cosmos/SPL/ESO; 119t: Réa/LAIF/ Gunnar Knechtel; 119b: Ciel et Espace/ESO; 120/121b: Reuters/Andres Forza; 120cr: Cosmos/ SPL/CSIRO; 121cr: Cosmos/SPL/NASA; 121b: Réa/AGStock/ R. Hamilton Smith; 122tl: Reuters/ Sheng Li; 122tr: Reuters/Charles Platiau; 123cr: Sipa/AP/Mike Alquinto; 123b: Réa/Panos/Jocelyn Carlin; 124t: Réa/Ropi/Featurechina; 124b: Réa/ Ropi/Featurechina/Chun Lei; 125t: Réa/Redux/Lou Dematteis; 125cr: Reuters/Ints Kalnins; 126t: Getty Images/Time and Life Images/Urbano Delvalle; 126b: Réa/Gilles Rolle; 127t: Cosmos/ SPL; 127b: AFP/Getty Images/Matt Cardy; 128t: Epicureans/Franck Bichon-Romain Grousseau; 128cr: AFP/Getty Images/DDP/Sebastien Willnow; 129t: Réa/Sylva Villerot; 129b: © Courtesy of Apple; 130: Service de Presse Yves Rossy Jetman; 131t: © Courtesy of Matt Harding; 131b: Sipa/Rex Features; 132t: © Sustainable Dance Club – Sustainable Dance Floor™; 132tl: Cosmos/SPL/André Geim; 132br: Corbis/Michael Macor; 133t: © MIT Media Lab, Massachusetts; 133b: Réa/The New York Times; 134tl: Réa/Benoît Decout; 134c: Réa/Benoît Decout; 135h: Réa/ Mario Fourmy; 135b: Réa/Ropi/Antonio Pisacreta; 136t: Cosmos/SPL/Alfred Pasieka; 136b: Réa/ Patrick Allard; 137t: Réa/Fanny Tondre; 137b: BSIP/Astier/CHU; 138tl: LookatSciences/NASA/ SDO/AIA; 138b: © ITER Organization; 139t & 139b: © ITER Organization; 140t: Corbis/EPA; 140b: Corbis/Science Faction/Peter Ginter; 141t: LookatSciences/Patrick Landmann; 141c: Cosmos/SPL; 141b: Collection Christophel/ 'Spiderman 2', 2004, Columbia TriStar Films; 142t: Gamma/Olivier Chouchana; 142b: Sipa/Rex Feature/Alex Segre; 143t: AFP/Getty Images/China Photos; 143b: Corbis/Atlantide Phototravel; 144tr: Cosmos/SPL/Volker Steger; 144/145t: Hemis.fr/ Stéphane Frances; 144br: Réa/Zuma/ Imaginechina, architect: Thomas Heatherwick; 145br: Hemis.fr/Tao Images, architect: He Jingtang; 146/147: Corbis/Science Faction/Peter Ginter; 148ct: Réa/Wilfried Maisy; 148b: Réa/ The New York Times/Wynn Thompson; 149l: AFP/Colin McPherson; 149r: Réa/Didier Maillac; 150t: Réa/ Hamilton; 150bl: Jean-Pierre Delagarde; 150br: Corbis/Andrew Brookes; 151t: Réa/Hanning/Dod; 151bl: © Courtesy of Apple; 151cr: Réa/The New York Times/Ed Zurga; 151br: Cosmos/SPL/ Torsten Wittmann; 152c: Rex Features; 152r: Réa/Benoît Decout; 152b: Cosmos/SPL; 153bl: © ITER Organization; 153tr: Cosmos/ Focus/Erich Speigelhalter; 153bd: Cosmos/SPL/
Mauro Fermariello.

Illustrations on pages 12tr and 13tl (segments of DNA illustrating epigenesis), 31 (reproductive and therapeutic cloning), 60 (expansion of the universe), 62t (ADSL), 68b (USB memory stick) and 110t (how we remember) – all by Grégoire Cirade.

THE ADVENTURE OF DISCOVERIES AND INVENTIONS
The Digital Age – 1995 to 2010
Published in 2012 in the United Kingdom by Vivat Direct Limited
(t/a Reader's Digest), 157 Edgware Road, London W2 2HR

Adapted from *L'Ére du Numérique*, part of a series entitled L'ÉPOPÉE DES
DÉCOUVERTES ET DES INVENTIONS, created in France by BOOKMAKER and
first published by Sélection du Reader's Digest, Paris, in 2011.

Translated from French by Peter Lewis

PROJECT TEAM
Series editor Christine Noble
Art editor Julie Bennett
Designer Martin Bennett
Consultant Ruth Binney
Proofreader Ron Pankhurst
Indexer Marie Lorimer

Colour origination FMG
Printed and bound in China

VIVAT DIRECT
Editorial director Julian Browne
Art director Anne-Marie Bulat
Managing editor Nina Hathway
Picture resource manager Sarah Stewart-Richardson
Technical account manager Dean Russell
Product production manager Claudette Bramble
Production controller Sandra Fuller

We are committed both to the quality of our products and the service we provide to our
customers. We value your comments, so please feel free to contact us on 0871 3511000
or via our website at **www.readersdigest.co.uk**

If you have any comments or suggestions about the content of our books, you can
email us at **gbeditorial@readersdigest.co.uk**

CONCEPT CODE: FR0104/IC/S
BOOK CODE: 642-015 UP0000-1
ISBN: 978-0-276-44527-9